LAST OF THE SUMMER WINE

LAST OF THE SUMMER WINE

by Roy Clarke

JOSEF WEINBERGER PLAYS

LONDON

LAST OF THE SUMMER WINE
First published in 2012
by Josef Weinberger Ltd
12-14 Mortimer Street, London W1T 3JJ
www.josef-weinberger.com / plays@jwmail.co.uk

The author asserts his moral right to be identified as the author of the work.

ISBN: 978 0 85676 304 5

Printed by Commercial Colour Press plc, Hainault, Essex

CAST OF CHARACTERS

in order of appearance

CLEGG

FOGGY

COMPO

GIFFORD BEWMONT

NORA BATTY

CONSTANCE

FLASH

ACT ONE

CLEGG's *dining room. One winter evening. It has a door right, which gives onto living room/kitchen/back door area and a door left, which leads to front door and upstairs. It's a room which has remained basically unchanged since the death of his wife a dozen years ago which is the main reason why the new wall units at the rear of stage stand out as conspicuously new. They are a rather flimsy, self-assembly network of shelves and storage units for hi-fi, books, etc. They are adjacent to, or perhaps surround, the serving hatch to the kitchen built into the rear wall.*

Someone has begun the laying of the table. The best white cloth hangs crisply from it almost to the floor. The best crockery is out.

CLEGG *enters from the kitchen, right, carrying a vase of flowers none too elegantly arranged. He is in the shirtsleeves and waistcoat of his best suit, an outfit in which he feels already a trifle claustrophobic. He pauses just inside the doorway to run a finger round inside of his tight shirt collar and to cast a less than enthusiastic glance at the room. He looks at his vase of flowers and calls out.*

CLEGG	Where do you want the flowers?
	(*The serving hatch slides open and* FOGGY's *head appears.*)
FOGGY	I'm a military man. Ask me where to stick a ren gun I'll tell you. But flowers – you're on your own.
CLEGG	I normally put them in the same place as most people round, here. In the cemetery.
FOGGY	Oh that's very co-operative. That's just the kind of sparkling high spirits we need

to ensure the successs of this evening's entertaining.

CLEGG   I don't like women in me house.

                         (FOGGY *glares and slams shut the hatch. He
                         appears very quickly through the doorway,
                         right. He takes the vase from* CLEGG *rather
                         ungraciously and begins seeking a place for
                         it on the table.*)

FOGGY   That's a nice thing to say. You don't like
                         women in the house. It's not like having
                         mice.

CLEGG   No? Then why do I have this primal fear
                         about getting one up me trouser leg?

FOGGY   Alright. Alright.

                         (FOGGY *throws a big sulk and goes and sinks
                         despondently in a chair where he folds his
                         arms and turns his face away.* CLEGG'S *seen
                         it all before. He groans quietly.*)

FOGGY   Let's just forget the whole thing.

CLEGG   You're sulking again.

FOGGY   I am not sulking again.

                         (FOGGY *sulks even harder.*)

FOGGY   I don't know why you should think I'm
                         sulking just because a friend proves
                         disappointing in your hour of need. Goes all
                         civilian. Loses his bottle.

CLEGG   You see. We're arguing already. We're tense.

FOGGY   I'm not tense. I'm versed in the practices of yoga. I'm damned if I'm tense.

         (FOGGY *turns his back even more resolutely. CLEGG goes to a drawer, takes out a folded paper bag, blows into it then walks close to FOGGY's sulky back and explodes it. FOGGY leaps out of his chair.*)

FOGGY   Waagh!!

CLEGG   You see. You're tense. You came out of that chair like spit off a griddle.

FOGGY   You damn fool. You should never do that to a combat soldier. I'm a trained killer you know. I could have snapped your neck. (*He snaps his fingers.*)

CLEGG   You were too busy snapping your own. Legs and arms in all directions. You looked like an exploding spider.

FOGGY   I deny that.

CLEGG   Because you're tense. We're both tense.

FOGGY   Why should we be tense?

CLEGG   Because you're bringing women to the house. To *my* house.

FOGGY   I can't take them to mine. I've only got a bedsit. A landlady who can eavesdrop in stereo. They're not just ears, she's got a woofer and tweeter.

CLEGG   I've seen it all before. The influence of women on a man's character. (*He looks round his room.*) Flowers on the table. Best

tablecloth out. I have to put a stiff collar on.
Musn't air me laundry over the oven door.

FOGGY   Hardly the place for it is it.

CLEGG   I like to know they're aired. It's like a good
             claret. Fresh underpants are best at room
             temperature.

FOGGY   Room temperature? They're practically
             baked. What are you growing in there?
             Orchids?

CLEGG   At my age I'm not growing anything. And
             I'm surprised you've any ambitions left in
             that direction.

FOGGY   I'm still in very choice condition for my
             age.

CLEGG   You won't be if you get involved with
             women.

FOGGY   You invite a lady properly chaperoned, for a
             bit of supper.

CLEGG   That's all it takes. it'll be the end of
             civilisation as we know it. All your freedom
             gone. They'll have you trussed and tied.

FOGGY   Aren't you being unnecessarily alarmist?

CLEGG   You're at the wrong age.

FOGGY   I wish you'd forget my age.

             (FOGGY *checks his watch and begins
             touching up the appearance of the table.*)

CLEGG   They'll have you Foggy.

FOGGY	A spot of supper that's all.
CLEGG	They're the thriftiest breed of women in the world round here. Once they get hold of a man they use everything but the squeak.
FOGGY	I shall dominate the situation. I shall be in command.
CLEGG	(*snorts*) Huh! Gordon Duckett was going to do that. Keep his woman in her place. You remember Big Gordon Duckett. Have you seen him lately? Looks like a retarded labrador.
FOGGY	I didn't rise to the heights of corporal accidentally you know.
CLEGG	You've no chance. Not with women.
FOGGY	I chased the Japs out of Burma.
CLEGG	Tiny little Japs. These are women. The Monstrous Regiment of Women. Women can even get Australians to the altar would you believe. Australians! Men who used to castrate sheep with their teeth.
FOGGY	Australians did?
CLEGG	Well. Not all Australians. I mean you can't see Rolf Harris can you. That's no place to get your beard fast.
	(FOGGY *begins pacing nervously*.)
FOGGY	Listen. A word in your ear from an old soldier. I hope we're not going to have any conversations on that level when the ladies get here.

CLEGG	Here you go you see. (*He runs a finger round his collar.*) The first whiff of female company and you've got not only your neck but your conversation in a stranglehold.
FOGGY	Good God there's enough to talk about without unnatural Australian practices.
CLEGG	Not as interesting though is it. I've got used to just the three of us being able to range reflectively on the oddities of the human condition.
FOGGY	Never mind the three of us. I'll be very grateful for just the two of us while the ladies are present. Talking about the oddities of the human condition, where is he tonight?
CLEGG	Don't worry about him.
FOGGY	I do worry about him. I worry about him turning up where he's not wanted.
CLEGG	Relax, Foggy. You're a bundle of premarital nerves.
	(FOGGY *turns on* CLEGG *sharply.*)
FOGGY	What do you mean premarital? Who mentioned marriage? Nobody mentioned marriage. What do you want to go and say a thing like that for?
CLEGG	(*grinning*) Relax.
FOGGY	I am relaxed. For an evening of female company I'm relaxed. Perhaps even for a few evenings of female company.
CLEGG	(*no longer grinning*) A few? You mean more than one?

FOGGY   Of course I mean more than one.

               (CLEGG *looks round his house and sighs.*)

FOGGY   But I'm damned if that amounts to marriage.
               Occasional female company will do us good.
               Sharpen us up. Add a touch of elegance this
               winter. Provided we can keep you-know-
               who out of the picture.

CLEGG   Isn't that a bit underhand?

FOGGY   (*grinning*) Yes. Isn't it. (*His grin slips.*)
               You're sure you didn't let anything slip
               about tonight. If he knows there's a free
               supper. Oh God let him not hear about this
               small free supper.

CLEGG   I've got used to the three of us. It seems
               unfair keeping him out.

FOGGY   It's not unfair. It's just damned difficult.

               (FOGGY *walks back towards the kitchen.*
               CLEGG, *left alone, looks round the room
               which he hardly recognises.*)

CLEGG   It's going to throw a spanner in our carefree
               lifestyles if you're always going to be
               entertaining women.

               (FOGGY *peers through the serving hatch.*)

FOGGY   What do you mean 'always' entertaining
               women. It must be five years since I
               entertained a woman.

               (FOGGY's *face withdraws. The hatch remains
               open.* CLEGG *sighs.*)

CLEGG	I hope you're not going to be at it every five years.

(CLEGG *approaches the table and stares at it sadly. He takes a crisp and crunches it.*)

FOGGY	(*off*) And leave the crisps alone.

(CLEGG *groans and folds his arms.* FOGGY'S *face appears.*)

FOGGY	Have you seen your cheese board?
CLEGG	I'm not surprised it's bored. I'm not too excited meself.

(FOGGY *shakes his head sadly.*)

FOGGY	Your heart's not in this is it. I ask for a little co-operation from a friend.
CLEGG	I have co-operated. I've turned me house upside down.
FOGGY	Don't exaggerate. You've got a bit of new furniture that's all.

(FOGGY *indicates the new wall units.*)

FOGGY	And very nice they look too. They've transformed this room. They've made a big alteration.
CLEGG	They've mades a big alteration to me bank balance I'll say that much for 'em.
FOGGY	Rubbish. They were a snip. I put you onto the bargain of the season here. Just look at this finish.

(FOGGY *leans through and pats a shelf. It collapses.* CLEGG *hurries to retrieve it.*)

CLEGG Will you go steady. It's not the kind of shelf you can just go putting things on.

FOGGY Have you got it in right? Didn't you follow the instructions?

CLEGG Have your seen the instructions? They were mostly in Chinese. And that was the easy bit.

FOGGY Just hold it there. I'll go round.

(FOGGY *hurries round and takes the shelf from* CLEGG.)

FOGGY Assembled in minutes. It said so on the box.

CLEGG That's another thing. I had a hell of a job opening the box.

(FOGGY *shakes his head in exasperation and sets to work.*)

FOGGY I tried to make things easy for you. I deliberately chose this model so you wouldn't have any bother.

CLEGG Oh it's no bother, I was all finished by four o'clock this morning. When the fire had gone out and the house was chilly. And you catch the eye of a photograph of somebody who's been a long time dead and you begin to think maybe they knew what they were doing after all.

(FOGGY *has replaced the shelf and steps back satisfied.*)

FOGGY   Well I'm sorry, I'm sure. It's just that
             I wanted your house to make a good
             impression.

CLEGG   She's a woman, Foggy. She's not going to
             be impressed by anything a man does in a
             house.

FOGGY   Constance is not like that.

CLEGG   They're you go again. Believing everything
             it says on the box. This way up. Pleasant
             female companion. Easily assembled in
             minutes.

FOGGY   Constance is a woman of some style
             and refinement. Cuts the crust off her
             sandwiches. Knows the French for vest.

CLEGG   She wipes the prongs on strange forks. Has
             ambitions towards fish knives. You'll be in
             trouble there Foggy. She's a snob.

FOGGY   I don't know why you should say that
             simply because the woman has high
             standards.

CLEGG   She's also engaged.

FOGGY   Unofficially.

CLEGG   For fourteen years it's been unofficially.

FOGGY   So she goes out with him occasionally.

CLEGG   Occasionally?

FOGGY   The man's a complete oaf. Unbearable.
             Pushy type. Wears his trousers out from the
             inside.

CLEGG	That's it, isn't it? Now we're getting to it.
FOGGY	To What?
CLEGG	To him. To Gifford Bewmont. The real reason for your sudden interest in Constance.
FOGGY	I don't know what you mean.

(FOGGY *hides his embarrassment by rearranging a few things on the table.*)

FOGGY	I like the woman. I thought a touch of female influence might shapen us up a bit. We were getting sloppy.
CLEGG	You're getting at him. It's him. It's Gifford Bewmont.
FOGGY	I invite her, properly chaperoned, for a spot of supper. It seem a perfectly ordinary thing to do.
CLEGG	Not for you. You're a bachelor to the roots of your money belt. It's not that you're pro- Constance. It's how much you're anti- Gifford Bewmont.
FOGGY	I can't stand him. Pushy. Loud and pushy.
CLEGG	We know that. But you don't have to get involved with his fiancee just to show him who's boss.
FOGGY	There's more to it than that.
CLEGG	Foggy. This is me you're talking to. Old Sloppy.
FOGGY	Anyway. She's not his fiancee.

CLEGG   For fourteen years they've been doing a
             good impression.

             (*The doorbell startles them.*)

FOGGY   Oh my God. They're early. I haven't found
             the cheese board yet.

CLEGG   Don't go to pieces. I'll get the door.

FOGGY   You can't go like that. Put your jacket on.

             (FOGGY *grabs* CLEGG *and hauls him back
             from the direction of the front door, left.*)

CLEGG   Steady on. It's not as if I've left me trousers
             off.

             (FOGGY *frogmarches* CLEGG *towards the
             living room door, right.*)

FOGGY   First impressions are important. Get
             yourself smartened up.

CLEGG   I'll say this for you Foggy. You know how
             to take these social occasions in your stride.

             (*They exit, right.* FOGGY *returns immediately
             to give his appearance a quick check in
             the mirror, then he begins fussing over the
             table. He makes same hasty attempts to
             improve the appearance of the flowers in
             the vase. The doorbell rings again more
             insistently.*)

FOGGY   Will you please get a move on that man.

             (CLEGG *enters pulling on his jacket.* FOGGY
             dives to assist him.)

CLEGG   I'm coming. I'm coming.

FOGGY   Put your tie straight.

CLEGG   The tie's straight. It's the windpipe that's
               twisted.

               (*Finally satisfied with* CLEGG's *tie,* FOGGY
               pushes CLEGG *on his way.* CLEGG *pauses at
               the door, left, and turns to* FOGGY.)

CLEGG   What is the French for vest?

FOGGY   What?

CLEGG   You said she knew the French for vest.

FOGGY   (*urging* CLEGG *on*) Chemise. Chemise.

CLEGG   She talks to you about vests?

FOGGY   We were walking. She stooped to pick a
               flower. "Excuse me" she said, flushing
               modestly. "My chemise is showing".

               (CLEGG *is looking cynical.*)

FOGGY   I turned away. Impressed by the delicacy
               of her feelings. It's so rare these days. She
               adjusted her dress. The incident was over.
               It brought us closer together. I found it
               charming.

CLEGG   Your days are numbered. You know that
               don't you.

FOGGY   Will you answer the door.

               (CLEGG *exits left. We hear him unbolting the
               front door.* FOGGY *meanwhile is calculating
               his position for maximum affect. A quick
               final check in the mirror and he begins
               trying out one or two casual poses for size.*

*Abandoning each one immediately as he
strives for the best. He produces a pipe from
his pocket as a final effect. He hears* CLEGG
open the door and FOGGY *fixes his face into
a smile of welcome. And this too feels not
quite right so he changes it once or twice,
ending up in some dreadfully uncomfortable
looking posture which he feels compelled
to maintain simply through having no more
time.* CLEGG *pokes his head through the
door.*)

CLEGG   Er – Foggy.

                  (FOGGY *signals impatiently, cutting off*
                  CLEGG'S *words.*)

FOGGY   Don't keep them waiting out there in the
                  hall. Bring them in. Bring them in.

                  (CLEGG *shrugs and withdraws his head.*
                  FOGGY *sets his face back into its stressful
                  smile. His pose collapses in despair as*
                  COMPO *saunters in grinning, his finger
                  pointing cheerfully at* FOGGY.)

COMPO   Hey up!

FOGGY   Oh no!

COMPO   Who's an old sly boots then?

                  (FOGGY *covers his eyes in horror.*)

FOGGY   Who told you? Who betrayed me?
                  (FOGGY *glares at the grinning* CLEGG *who
                  has just re-entered, left.* COMPO *approaches
                  the table.*)

COMPO   Having a bit a supper are we?

(FOGGY *hurries to haul* COMPO *away.*)

FOGGY   No are are not. Keep your hands off. I've seen what you can do to a well-laid table. Oh my God! Look at the state he's in. Why is he always dressed for an earthquake?

(*He slaps* COMPO'S *hand away from the table.*)

COMPO   Tha should a said if it were formal.

FOGGY   I should have said nothing about it. I did say nothing about it. (*Turns on* CLEGG.) And what's more I asked certain other parties to say nothing about it.

CLEGG   That's true. I remember now. And why I remember now is because you spent most of yesterday and the greater part of today ordering me to say nothing about it.

FOGGY   So how come he turns up on your doorstep just at the crucial moment?

(CLEGG *puts a hand over his heart and adopts his most innocent expression.*)

CLEGG   Just lucky I guess.

(FOGGY *whips round in horror as he hears* COMPO *crunch a crisp.*)

FOGGY   Come away.

(FOGGY *grabs* COMPO *by collar and coat-tail and begins marching him round round the table and then towards the door, left.*)

COMPO   Hey up! Where we going?

FOGGY	You're going back through the door.
COMPO	That's charming isn't it! Thrown out! For one lousy crisp!

(CLEGG *intervenes to bar their way.*)

CLEGG	You can't just throw him out.
COMPO	Tha should listen to Cleggy. He knows what he's talking about.
FOGGY	I'm not just going to throw him out. I'm going to throw him as far as I can possibly reach.

(COMPO'S *resistance is increasing now and halting* FOGGY'S *progress as they strain and struggle.* COMPO *is now lying on his back.*)

COMPO	He's excitable tonight isn't he.
CLEGG	Yes I noticed that.
FOGGY	Don't just stand there. Give me a hand somebody. (COMPO *offers his hand.*) Not you.
CLEGG	Listen Foggy. Can't we came to some arrangement?
FOGGY	Him. Out. That's the arrangement.
CLEGG	Suppose he offered to pay you the crisp back.
COMPO	Will tha take a cheque? Mind me jacket.
FOGGY	You call this a jacket.

(COMPO *wriggles free of his jacket and leaves* FOGGY *holding it.*)

FOGGY   Oh my God! Look at his shirt.

COMPO   Tha's torn it.

FOGGY   *I've* torn it?

COMPO   There he goes, listen. He's admitting it.

FOGGY   How can you turn out in a shirt like that?

COMPO   Well normally it's hidden under me coat isn't it. I didn't expect some fool to be pulling me jacket off. Supposed to be a mate a mine. Trying to throw me out.

(COMPO *goes into a big sad act.*)

COMPO   'Cos I'm Not wanted. 'Cos I'm poor. And underprivileged. 'Cos I'm an orphan. And I've lost me best ferret and ms elbow creaks. I'm not wanted. Go on. say it.

CLEGG / FOGGY (*in mock sympathy*) Aww!

COMPO   It does. I'm not lying. Me elbow creaks. Have a listen. Alright. Don't have a listen. If I'm not wanted why don't you say it to me face.

(FOGGY *bends close towards* COMPO's *face.*)

FOGGY   You're not wanted.

COMPO   Tha dunt have to be in such a blasted hurry. Tha could a thought about it a bit.

FOGGY   I've thought about it. Believe me I've thought about it. Get your coat on.

COMPO   Tha can't send me out in the pouring rain.

FOGGY   Don't lie to me, it's a beautiful night.

COMPO   It's a beautiful night for thee. Tha's going to
             be stuffing thee face.

FOGGY   We'll save you some. Come back tomorrow
             we'll give you a doggy bag.

             (COMPO *appeals dramatically to* CLEGG.)

COMPO   Why dun't he like me? Why dun't he like
             me?

CLEGG   It's nothing personal. It's only because
             you're horrible and scruffy.

             (COMPO *nods, apparently perfectly satisfied
             with the explanation.*)

COMPO   He should have said.

FOGGY   Get him out of here.

COMPO   He likes me really.

CLEGG   Deep down.

             (COMPO *approaches* FOGGY *smiling coyly.*)

COMPO   Give us a kiss.

FOGGY   Go!

COMPO   No listen. I can't go out there. There's all
             sorts a fellers roaming the streets.

FOGGY   Get your coat on. No more excuses.

COMPO   I'm telling thee. The streets are full of little groups of excited husbands looking for the Flasher. They grabbed me three times on me way here. I ask you. Do I look like a Flasher?

                 (*He waits confidently for their agreement. It fails to come.*)

COMPO   Oh that's charming isn't it.

CLEGG   Well we don't know what the Flasher looks like do we. I mean some of the descriptions have been exaggerated to say the least.

FOGGY   Creepy swine! He's not on the prowl tonight is he? Oh My God! There's Constance and her auntie out there somewhere.

CLEGG   The thing is to look at his face. Keep looking at his face.

COMPO   He'll be lying low tonight. There's too many blokes about. Anything he pulls out tonight is going to get trampled to death.

FOGGY   Well I'm relieved to hear somebody's had the initiative to organise counter measures. If I wasn't occupied here I'd pop along and give them the benefit of my night patrol activities.

COMPO   They don't need thee Foggy. Some other ex-army big head's promoted himself in charge.

FOGGY   I hope he's a natural leader. Is it anyone we know?

COMPO   It's that Gifford Bewmont.

FOGGY   That fool. Trust him to elbow his way to the top. You know what he's doing don't you. He's trying to impress Constance.

CLEGG   Well he's had his opportunity. They've been engaged for fourteen years.

COMPO   Big dosy closet. He had me under a lamp post for questioning.

FOGGY   Overkill, you see. Heavy handed. Typical. The man has no sublety.

COMPO   Cheeky beggar. Do you know what he said to me? Have you been exposing yourself to two ladies outside the fish shop. I thought bloody hell. That's all. you need. Salt and vinegar on it.

FOGGY   The man's so pushy. And I hate his nose. Have you seen his nose? He's got these little hairs . . . How did you establish your innocence?

COMPO   I was too short to fit the description. (*Adding hastily.*) In height. In height.

CLEGG   Bragging again.

COMPO   So they let me go. But I'm not off out there again till that lot's buggered off. They're dangerous. You daren't even reach for your trouser pocket out there tonight.

FOGGY   Well you can't stay here in that condition. No way. That's out. No excuses.

CLEGG   There is en alternative, Foggy. We could smarten him up a bit.

(COMPO *grins amiably while* FOGGY *and* CLEGG *circle him.*)

FOGGY   I like a challenge but this is . . .

COMPO   I could wear Cleggy's other suit.

CLEGG   It's at the cleaners.

(FOGGY *throws up his hands in despair.*)

FOGGY   It's hopeless you see.

CLEGG   No. There must be something he can wear. I'll take him upstairs. Have a look in the wardrobe.

(*As* CLEGG *leads the way out through the door, left,* FOGGY *has turned his back to indicate his distrust of the whole procedure.* COMPO *nips back to the table and snatches another crisp. He doesn't crunch it until he gets back to the doorway, left. There he pops it in his mouth through a mischievous grin.* FOGGY *spins round when he hears the crunch.*)

FOGGY   I heard that . . .

(*But* COMPO *has gone.* FOGGY *hurries to check the table, calling upstairs as he does so.*)

FOGGY   If he's going to stay you'll, have to keep him under control.

(*An answering raspberry comes floating back.* FOGGY *groans.*)

FOGGY   Just what I need to create a good impression. It's conversation like . . .

(*Imitates the raspberry*.) . . . that's really
going to make this evening go with a
swing. He's going to shatter the ambience
completely. I had this vision of a small oasis
of refinement. The clink of sherry glasses.
A gentle passing of the After Eights. The
eyes of the ladies glittering with interest
and appreciation of my army reminiscences.
Well that's up the Swanee now. He'll be
butting in with his own army stories and
oh my God we know what they're like. (*He
shouts up at the ceiling*.) You can shut up
about your army stories.

(*Overcome by dread,* FOGGY *rests a hand
for support on the wall unit. Another shelf
collapses*.)

FOGGY   Damnation! (*He sets to on the replacing
of it*.) I'm surrounded by civilian
incompetence.

(*The doorbell rings and throws him into
a panic. He's in a position where he's just
on the point of refixing the shelf and he's
reluctant to let it go*.)

FOGGY   The bell – Er – can you get . . . They're
here. Can somebody come down and hold
this. Or get the door. Get the door. Talk to
yourself, Foggy.

(*He lets go of the shelf. It collapses again.
He runs back to it and props it temporarily
with the aid of a book from another and
firmer section of the wall unit. He darts
for a quick check of his appearance in the
mirror. The bell rings again*.)

CLEGG   (*off*) There's somebody at the door.

(FOGGY *tries to suppress the noise of his frustration as he glares up at the ceiling.*)

FOGGY
I know there's somebody at the door.

(FOGGY *exits left, smoothing down his hair. We hear a scamper of feet downstairs and* FOGGY *is almost bowled over by* COMPO *in his long johns who enters left, rapidly, and backs away from* CLEGG'S *pursuit in alarm.*)

COMPO
I'm not wearing that.

FOGGY
What's he doing? Look at him. Oh my God! Get him back upstairs. Get some clothes on him. The ladies are at the door.

COMPO
I'm not wearing a thing like that.

FOGGY
(*covers his eyes*) Stop waving your arms about. stop waving everything about!

(CLEGG *is holding a kilt.* COMPO *backs away again.*)

CLEGG
It's only a kilt. It belongs to Mrs Clegg, but . . . Men wear kilts.

COMPO
Not round these parts they don't.

(FOGGY *snatches the kilt and attempts to drape it round* COMPO'S *lower half.*)

FOGGY
It's just round those parts they do. Get 'em covered up.

(COMPO *dodges away round the table.*)

FOGGY
Don't stand like that near the table. Get him away from the table. There are some things you don't ever want to see in a sideplace.

(*They begin to advance on* COMPO *from
opposite ends of the table.* COMPO *picks up
the plate of mints in self-defence and holds
it high, threatening its destruction.*)

COMPO   Keep away.

FOGGY   The mints. Don't let him drop the After
             Eight mints.

             (*They freeze at the temporary stalemate.*)

COMPO   Tha's not getting me in a skirt.

CLEGG   It's a kilt.

COMPO   Well up thee kilt.

FOGGY   Couldn't you find any trousers to fit him?

CLEGG   There's nothing. He's the wrong shape. You
             can see what a shape he is.

FOGGY   That's the trouble. We can see to damn
             plainly whet shape he is.

COMPO   Keep away.

FOGGY   Go steady with those mints.

CLEGG   I've got a sports jacket to fit him. And
             there's this kilt the wife used to wear . . .

COMPO   I telled thee it were a skirt.

CLEGG   Kilts are unisex. And there's an old frilly
             blouse of hers.

COMPO   Listenat him. He wants me in a blouse now.

CLEGG   Under the sports jacket it'll look just like
                 what the well dressed Scotman wears of an
                 evening.

COMPO   No!

                 (*The bell rings again, startling everybody,
                 especially* COMPO *who drops the plate of
                 mints.*)

COMPO   Aargh!

FOGGY   Get him! Don't tread on the mints. But get
                 him.

                 (*As they move towards him,* COMPO *dives
                 under the table and remains there, hidden
                 by the folds of the table cloth. The bell rings
                 again.*)

FOGGY   No. Wait! Wait!! Leave him under there.
                 Where he's out of sight. I'll let the ladies in.
                 (*He points to the door, right.*) I'll take 'em
                 straight through to the living room and then
                 you can get him out of there and if he won't
                 wear the kilt you can throw him outside
                 in his long johns for all I care. And let's
                 see him talk his way out of that when he's
                 picked up for a flasher.

                 (*As* FOGGY *walks towards the door, left,*
                 COMPO *makes a rude noise.*)

FOGGY   And keep him quiet.

                 (FOGGY *exits left and we hear the front door
                 being opened.*)

COMPO   Has he gone?

CLEGG   Keep quiet.

COMPO   I can't stay under here.

CLEGG   It's only for a minute.

COMPO   Give us a crisp.

CLEGG   I'm not supposed to feed you.

COMPO   It's your house.

CLEGG   Ah yes. But it's temporarily under martial
             law.

             (FOGGY *re-enters, left, looking less than
             pleased.*)

FOGGY   It's old Bicycle Clips. Gifford Bewmont
             at his most officious on your doorstep.
             Demands to see the owner of the house.

             (GIFFORD *appears in the doorway, left,
             in his Special Constable's uniform and
             bicycle clips. He has a bugle slung over his
             shoulder on a cord and it hangs somewhere
             round his knees. He is* FOGGY's *age but
             stockier. He has the mannerisms of a
             lifelong know-it-all and instinctive over-
             dramatiser.*)

GIFFORD   Don't anybody move. I want you to hear
             this.

FOGGY   Oh get on with it.

             (FOGGY *begins retrieving the after dinner
             mints.* GIFFORD *stands to attention and
             brings the bugle to his lips with a Military
             flourish. He puffs out his cheeks and
             produces an earsplitting toot or two. We
             hear a yelp of surprise from under the table
             and the sound of* COMPO *cracking his head.*)

GIFFORD   What was that?

CLEGG   Sounded like a bugle to me, Gifford. But if
               you want the name of the tune you'll have to
               play more than that.

GIFFORD   Not this. I heard a yelp. Sounded like a yelp.
               Hello, I thought. That's a yelp.

CLEGG   Gifford heard a yelp.

FOGGY   That was me picking these things up. I
               pricked. my finger.

               (FOGGY *begins sucking his finger*.)

GIFFORD   On an after dinner mint?

FOGGY   A splinter on the floor. Get on with your
               business. What have you come intruding in
               here for?

               (GIFFORD *draws himself up to his full
               dignity*.)

CLEGG   Not that it's not kind of you to pop in an'
               give us a tune on your bugle.

GIFFORD   That was no tune. Said he was growing
               suspicion that certain parties in this billet
               are trying to take the wee-wee. That was a
               signal. (*He thrusts his face near* CLEGG'S.)
               Comprenday? A signal. A police-type signal
               which you failed to recognise possibly
               owing to the absense of a revolving blue
               light on the top of my bleeding hat.

               (FOGGY *is looking at his plate of rescued
               mints with a concerned expression*.)

FOGGY   There's one missing.

(Gifford's *expression is sneering.* Foggy
*looks round the floor behind the table then
lifts a corner of the cloth and announces in
an accusing tone.*)

FOGGY   Where can it have gone I wonder.

GIFFORD   He counts his after dinner mints?

CLEGG   He's always had a reckless streak.

FOGGY   I happen to know how many there are in a
             pack that's all.

             (FOGGY *blows the dust off the plate of mints
             and puts it back on the table.*)

GIFFORD   In order to make this a community safe
             to count after dinner mints in. (GIFFORD
             sniggers behind his hand.) Some of us
             are giving free time voluntarily as special
             constables.

FOGGY   Pushy. Needs the uniform.

GIFFORD   I'm no stranger to uniform.

FOGGY   I spent a lifetime in uniform.

GIFFORD   Royal Engineers! Call that a uniform?

FOGGY   We were there where the action was. Which
             is more than you can say for the dainty
             Royal Signals.

(*They are squaring up to each other, their jaws thrust out, threatening.*)

FOGGY   Ladylike shower.

GIFFORD   Watch it, Dewhirst!

(CLEGG *separates them by tugging* GIFFORD *away by his bugle.*)

CLEGG   Gifford. Will you kindly explain what you're doing here on the end of this bugle.

FOGGY   I'll tell you what he's doing here. He's poking his nose in because it's worrying him to death that I'm entertaining a lady whose affections he's been toying with for the past fourteen years.

GIFFORD   Toying with! What do you mean toying with? Constance and I are engaged.

FOGGY   You've had your opportunity, Bewmont.

CLEGG   I should think he has in fourteen years.

GIFFORD   Typical slimy Royal Engineers' trick. Taking advantages of a bloke's bint while he's on duty.

CLEGG   Not exactly taking advantage Gifford. Her aunty's coming. She's well chaperoned.

FOGGY   Duty? What duty?

GIFFORD   The apprehension of the dirty bugger that's leaping about round here trouserless and waving his dong during the hours of darkness to the discomfort of the female population.

(*At the mention of the word 'trouserless'
both* CLEGG *and* FOGGY *move sheepishly
to afford better cover to* COMPO *under the
table.*)

FOGGY   In darkness?

GIFFORD   From late evening onwards. He has the MO
             of a barn owl.

CLEGG   Justa Dong at Twilight I can understand.
             But in the darkness how come he's such a
             discomfort to the female population?

GIFFORD   At the moment he strikes the bugger's
             illuminated. Got some kind of lighting
             arrangement. Comes on all floodlit, doesn't
             he.

             (COMPO *yawns loudly under the table.* FOGGY
             is compelled to pretend he's responsible.)

GIFFORD   You find this boring?

FOGGY   No.

             (*Another yawn from* COMPO *which* FOGGY
             tries to cover.)

GIFFORD   Been having late nights, have we?

FOGGY   No. Yes. That's it.

GIFFORD   Been wandering the streets trouserless, have
             we?

FOGGY   How dare you.

GIFFORD   Well if it's you I shall have you, Dewhirst.

FOGGY   Damned cheek.

CLEGG   Both cheeks by the sound of it.

GIFFORD   I shall have you . . . (*He taps his forehead
                   slyly*.) . . . because I've got this area
                   covered. What with foot patrols of
                   concerned citizens and me on my Hercules
                   bicycle. Nobody moves in the streets
                   tonight without Gifford Bewmont being in
                   the know. Woe betide the mucky hooligan
                   caught trouserless tonight.

                   (*Behind* GIFFORD'S *back,* COMPO'S *face peers
                   out from under the table cloth. It shows
                   every sign of concern at the threats* GIFFORD
                   is outlining.)

GIFFORD   I'll teach him to wear more with his raincoat
                   than balaclava and boots.

                   (*The mention of balaclava prompts* COMPO *to
                   pull down his cap comforter until it covers
                   his face. Even with his face hidden we can
                   still gain an impression of his reactions
                   to* GIFFORD'S *threats by the way his head
                   moves. Both* CLEGG *and* FOGGY, *who can
                   see* COMPO'S *performance, are watching it
                   spellbound, fearful of his being discovered.*)

GIFFORD   I'll see he gets more on his wedding tackle
                   than a forty watt bulb. There are strong
                   men with gloves under my command not
                   averse to giving him a painful twank where
                   necessary to subdue him.

                   (COMPO *begins creeping stealthily out from
                   the cover of the table making for the door,
                   left.* CLEGG *and* FOGGY *flinch at the risk he is
                   taking.*)

GIFFORD   And while it's normal to lead a prisoner
                   jailwards by means of a steady pressure on

his elbow, in these unusual circumstances
you might have to grab what's available.

(*We see* COMPO *shuddering at the thought.*)

GIFFORD   So. You heard the signal. That sequence of
toots on the bugle indicating the flasher has
been seen. At the sound of which I expect
all men of goodwill to drop whatever they
might be doing. (*He glares at* FOGGY.)
Especially if they're doing it with somebody
else's bint. And get themselves out in the
streets to lend a hand.

(GIFFORD *is about to turn round.* COMPO *is
still only half way to the door.* CLEGG *and*
FOGGY *leap to distract* GIFFORD.)

CLEGG   You can rely on us Gifford.

FOGGY   You wouldn't like to run through that signal
again.

GIFFORD   Let go the hand. Let go the hand.

CLEGG   Really neat little bugle Gifford.

GIFFORD   Watch the bugle. Let go the bugle.

FOGGY   Plays it entirely with his mouth, right
Gifford?

GIFFORD   Will you take your maulers off.

(GIFFORD *breaks away, straightens his cap
and turns in time to see* COMPO'S *trouserless
rear going through the door.*)

GIFFORD   What the hell do you think you're playing
at. There he goes. It's him!

(*At* GIFFORD'S *shriek,* COMPO *gets to his feet and scarpers through the front door doing his own subdued wailing.* GIFFORD *takes a few steps in pursuit, gets the bugle trapped between his legs. Hops about wildly on the spot trying to free himself.*)

GIFFORD   It's him by God. It's him!

(CLEGG *and* FOGGY *hurry to* GIFFORD'S *aid with the intention of securing him even more firmly in the entanglements of the bugle.*)

GIFFORD   Get after him!

CLEGG   Just put your leg through here, Gifford.

GIFFORD   Don't let him get away.

FOGGY   The signal, Gifford. Make the signal.

(*From outside come two sets of female shrieks.* COMPO *still with his hat covering his face comes running back in again through the door, left. He gallops across stage and exits, right, pursued by* NORA BATTY *prepared to do battle with her umbrella. She exits right, as* GIFFORD *renews his struggles to get free only to get entangled even further with the aid of* FOGGY *and* CLEGG.)

GIFFORD   Stop him.

CLEGG   You nearly had him there Gifford.

FOGGY   The signal. Make the signal.

(GIFFORD'S *attempts to get the bugle to his lips are complicated in the extreme now, entangled round him as it is. It's somewhere between his legs and he has to bend*

strangely and waddle duck fashion as he
tries to blow it. The best he can manage are
a few absurd squeaks from the instrument.
He's stIll twisting and waddling and trying
to blow it as CONSTANCE *enters to lean*
weakly in the doorway.)

CONSTANCE   Gifford. What are you doing here?

GIFFORD   I should be asking you that.

(*He goes gamely back to his squeaky*
blowing as NORA *enters, right.*)

NORA   Gone. out the back door and away. Up the
                 street like a squirrel.

(*She stands and watches* GIFFORD'S
performance scornfully.)

NORA   Three grown men can't stop him. Why is he
                 still playing with his trumpet?

CONSTANCE   Oh it was awful.

NORA   It was moving too fast to be awful.
                 Fortunately everything was just a blur.

CONSTANCE   When he opened the door I nearly died.

NORA   Oh come off it our Connie. You've seen
                 a bloke in his underpants before. (*She*
                 indicates GIFFORD.) Even after fourteen
                 years engaged to this you must have got that
                 far.

CONSTANCE   Aunty Nora!

(CONSTANCE *pats heir hair primly.* GIFFORD
struggles free of his entanglements. He
hurries in belated pursuit of COMPO *through*
the door, right. He returns again.)

GIFFORD	Just remember we're engaged.
NORA	Remember? How can she forget? You've practically made a damned career out of it.
CONSTANCE	We never actually bought a ring, Gifford.
	(*She examines her ring finger.*)
GIFFORD	Soon as I see the right ring. I'm looking. You know I'm looking. (*He snarls at the grinning* FOGGY.) I'll be back.
	(GIFFORD *exits, right. We hear the fading toots of his bugle.* FOGGY *and* CLEGG *exchange a nervous glance.*)
CONSTANCE	I hope they catch him. Who was it? What was he doing in here?
CLEGG	Search me. Complete stranger to us.
FOGGY	Absolutely.
NORA	Well from where I was looking I can't say the face was familiar.
FOGGY	Must have sneaked in behind Gifford, when he left the door open.
CONSTANCE	Peculiar.
FOGGY	I always thought so. Well. Now the excitement's over, ladies perhaps you'd care to take your coats upstairs.
NORA	They'll be alright down here.
FOGGY	Perhaps use the bathroom.
NORA	It wasn't that exciting.

(FOGGY *groans then fixes his face into what is meant to be a reassuring smile of welcome.*)

FOGGY   My apologies for all these upsets ladies. Come along through to the living room. Make yourselves comfortable.

(CLEGG *eases his tight collar with a finger.* FOGGY *holds the door, right, for the ladies.*)

FOGGY   Constance.

NORA   (*aside to* CONSTANCE) Show me a man with good manners and I'll show you somebody who'll have your blouse unbuttoned if you're not careful.

CONSTANCE   Just lead the way through, Aunty Nora.

NORA   Let him lead the way through. God knows who else is lurking through there without his trousers.

FOGGY   I can assure you madam.

NORA   I'll cripple him if there is.

(NORA *exits right, her brolly at the ready.* CONSTANCE *pauses to impress* FOGGY *in the doorway.*)

CONSTANCE   Why in this house? Who could it have been?

FOGGY   Some passing pervert.

CONSTANCE   Long as he's not based here.

(CONSTANCE *exits, right.* FOGGY *grabs the opportunity for a word with* CLEGG.)

FOGGY   Leave your collar alone. Nip upstairs and
                 bring him some clothes down here. We've
                 got to sneak them out to him somehow.

CLEGG   How? With the women through there?

FOGGY   Get his clothes down here then we've got to
                 get the women upstairs. Out the way.

CLEGG   Get the women upstairs? Listen. That
                 sounds very dodgy. I tell you this as a News
                 of the World reader.

FOGGY   Go and fetch him same clothes. Before he
                 gets picked up by Gifford Bewmont and his
                 Merry Men.

                 (CLEGG *exits, left. He can be heard pounding
                 upstairs.* FOGGY *fixes his smile on again and
                 exits, right, to join the ladies.*)

FOGGY   Now then ladies. I can offer you a robust
                 little sherry.

                 (CLEGG *can be heard returning downstairs
                 again. He enters, left, after making sure the
                 coast is clear. He is carrying a well-filled
                 plastic carrier which he now seeks to hide.
                 He tries stuffing it under a chair. Decides
                 against this and takes it try the wall unit.
                 He opens a cupboard door which comes
                 away in his hand. The clatter makes him
                 panic guiltily. He stuffs his carrier into the
                 cupboard and makes over-hasty attempts
                 to get, the door back on. He jumps a foot
                 as* FOGGY *suddenly raps open the serving
                 hatch.*)

FOGGY   Will you bring scome crisps and nuts and
                 things.

(FOGGY *slams the hatch shut.* CLEGG *clutches his pounding heart then using the cupboard door as a tray, he loads one or two things onto it and bears it through the door, right, like an experienced waiter. He returns almost immediately with his tray empty and begins trying to get it back into place as a cupboard door. He leaps in fright again as* FOGGY *slams open the hatch.*)

FOGGY   What are you leaping about for? Why have you gone white?

CLEGG   Will you stop popping up like that.

FOGGY   Did you get him some clothes?

CLEGG   Yes.

FOGGY   Well done that man. Right. Listen. The next thing we've got to do is while I'm in the living room entertaining the ladies you've got to come in with some cast iron reason for getting us all upstairs.

CLEGG   Like what, for instance?

FOGGY   Oh come on now Cleggy. Finger out. Don't let me have to think of everything.

(FOGGY *slams the hatch shut again.* CLEGG *throws up his hands in despair, in one of which he finds he's still clutching the cupboard door. He glares at in disgust. He has one more try at fixing it back on. He gives it a tap to get it into place. An upper shelf of the unit collapses limply. Suppressing a scream,* CLEGG *leans the door against the unit and abandons it. He comes nearer front of stage and begins pacing as he tries to work out his next move.*)

CLEGG   A cast iron reason for getting them all
                upstairs he says. The view. What view?
                Anyway it's dark. That's it! The lights.
                Come up and see the lights. That major
                cluster over there is Wagstaff's Bakery. That
                ought to hold them spellbound.

                (*He abandons that idea and resumes his
                pacing, eying the door, right, nervously
                where any moment he's expected to make his
                entrance with some fascinating lure to get
                them upstairs.*)

CLEGG   Come on Clegg. Think. What do men say to
                women to get them upstairs? (*His expression
                goes very sour.*) Well that's out. What gets
                Yorkshire women upstairs? Yorkshire men
                usually. I can't walk in there and invite
                women upstairs. You feel such a fool if
                they refuse. And worse still if they accept.
                I was married for a long time. What used to
                put a spring in my wife's step and prompt
                her towards the bedroom? Papering the
                ceiling. That's it. They can't resist a bit of
                decorating. They lie there on honsymoon
                staring at the ceiling. It seem to get in their
                bloodstream.

                (*He gives his collar a final tug, composes
                himself and exits, right.*)

CLEGG   (*loudly*) I'm going to have to do something
                about that bedroom paper. I don't know
                what colour goes with a faded red
                candlewick bedspread.

                (*After barely a moment's pause, the women
                enter, right and troop across stage,* NORA
                leading the way.)

NORA   He wants to try a pastel shade.

CONSTANCE

You can call me old fashioned but I don't think you can beat white.

NORA

You are old fashioned. White always goes yellow. It's like living in Hong Kong.

(*They exit, left and can be heard tramping upstairs.* FOGGY *is following them. He turns to glare at the smirking self-satisfied* CLEGG.)

FOGGY

Clever beggar! Aright. I'll keep them chatting upstairs. Take him his clothes out the back.

CLEGG

Suppose he's not there. Suppose he comes round the other way?

FOGGY

Don't panic. I'll leave him this front door open in case he comes in this way.

(FOGGY *exits, left. We hear him open the front door and then climb the stairs.* CLEGG *retrieves his carrier from behind the loose cupboard door which he props up again then* CLEGG *tiptoes from the room, exiting right, with the carrier. In the few seconds the stage is empty a few distant toots on the bugle are heard. A figure enters the front door rapidly and slams it behind him. We can hear the bolts being driven home, then the* FLASHER'S *head in a balaclava peers in cautiously through the door, left. Seeing the room empty he tiptoes in. A tall figure, of approximately* FOGGY'S *build, he wears an enormous raincoat down to his feet. It's all securely buttoned and belted. He peels off his balaclava and mops his brow with a handkerchief. He tiptoes across to the door, right, pausing only to wolf an after dinner mint which causes him to frown and pick bits of fluff from his teeth delicately. He peers through the door, right, and returns to take another mint which he holds up to the light. He frowns and blows the fluff off before returning it to its plate. He hesitates over his choice of something else from the table and finally selects a stick of celery which he salts fastidiously, bites and salts again. He takes it on a journey round the room, He pauses before the books in the wall unit, reading their titles. He's still holding the balaclava, so he holds the celery in his mouth in order to have a free hand with which he takes out the book which is propping the shelf. The shelf collapses and he panics a bit and tries to reassemble things. He's caught like this with celery in his mouth as* COMPO *and* CLEGG *enter, right.)*

COMPO   Tha's not getting me in that frock.

CLEGG   We can't get your own clothes. The women are upstairs.

             (All three parties freeze at the sight of each other.)

COMPO   Hey up! There's a bloke with celery in his mouth.

CLEGG   Yes. I noticed that.

             (The FLASHER *regains his wits. He stuffs his balaclava into his pocket, removes his celery and advances smiling, hand out stretched in greeting, trying to hide his panic.)*

FLASHER   Good evening gentlemen!

(*Completely bemused, they shake hands formally.*)

COMPO   Evening!

CLEGG   Evening!

(COMPO *and* CLEGG *look at each other, a trifle awed by the absurdity of the situation. The* FLASHER *puts a finger to his lips indicating silence.* COMPO *takes* CLEGG'S *carrier bag and holds it in front of himself discretely. The* FLASHER *exits, right, for a moment as he inspects the premises.*)

COMPO   What's he doing here?

(CLEGG *shrugs. The* FLASHER *returns through the door, right.*)

FLASHER   Are we alone? You can tell me, I've got an honest face.

(*He gives them a close up of it in turn, wearing a smile designed to reassure but which fails dismally.*)

FLASHER   Don't tell me that's no honest face. Look at the eyes. Look at the eyes.

CLEGG   The customary two.

FLASHER   But frank and friendly. Right? Set wide apart. Look at that then. Measure it. (*He measures it with his celery.*) None of your close together, shifty about that lot. Right.

COMPO   Listen Jack. I don't want to be a wet blanket about this but what are you doing in people's houses?

FLASHER	I'm glad you asked me that. There's nobody appreciates frankness more than me. Incidentally, you know you've got fluff on your after dinner mints. I tell you this not in any spirit of criticism . . . (*He puts an arm round them, they back away.*) . . . but as someone who would be a friend.
COMPO	Ask him what he's got under thar raincoat.
FLASHER	Look who's talking.
COMPO	Ask him.
CLEGG	You can't ask a feller a thing like that.
COMPO	If he's got a thing like that he's the feller, they're all looking for.
CLEGG	Oh God! This collar's killing me.
COMPO	Ask him what he's doing here.
FLASHER	There's a perfectly simple explanation. I had it on the tip of me tongue.
CLEGG	Amnesia. He's got amnesia.
COMPO	Stop making excuses for him. He hasn't got amnesia.
FLASHER	No. No. I tell a lie. It's coming back to me. (*He picks up a book discarded earlier and raises it triumphantly.*)
FLASHER	Encyclopaedias.
COMPO	Tha what?
FLASHER	That's what I'm selling. Encyclopaedias.

CLEGG   I'll take one.

COMPO   Don't be so daft. He's not really selling
             encyclopaedias.

CLEGG   I can't help it. I've got no sales resistance.

COMPO   If he's selling encyclopaedias, where are
             they then?

FLASHER   Ah well, We get the orders first. That
             way we know how many to print. You
             can't go churning out reams of bleeding
             encyclopaedias on the off chance some
             mutton's going to buy one.

COMPO   He's the Flasher. Look at that coat. He's the
             Flasher. We ought to turn him in.

CLEGG   We can't turn him in.

COMPO   It'll stop 'em thinking it's me. Why can't we
             turn him in?

             (CLEGG, *stumped for an answer, shrugs*.)

CLEGG   He's got an honest face.

COMPO   Has he hell as like. Besides it's not his face
             he's been showing is it.

CLEGG   He's frightened. He's got the same look in
             his eyes as a swallow I once found trapped
             in me window.

             (COMPO *sighs and gives up the argument.
             They hear feet clattering down the stairs*.)

CLEGG   It's the women. Got under the table.

(COMPO *and the* FLASHER *eye each other's dress dubiously for a split second before diving to share the space under the table.* CLEGG *begins whistling innocently as* FOGGY *enters, left.*)

FOGGY   Will you get a move on. I'm fed up of talking wallpaper.

CLEGG   There's a bit of a snag come up, Foggy.

FOGGY   Isn't he dressed yet?

(COMPO *emerges from under the table.*)

COMPO   No. And he's not going to flaming be in these.

(*He holds up the carrier.*)

FOGGY   He's got no choice. Leave him to it. Come upstairs and give me a hand with these women. They're moving your furniture about. They feel sure you'll like the change.

CLEGG   Oh God! Listen Foggy. I can't come up just yet.

FOGGY   Why ever not?

(*With quiet satisfaction at the idea of disconcerting* FOGGY, COMPO *lifts up the tablecloth.*)

COMPO   This is why not.

(*The* FLASHER *smiles sheepishly.*)

FOGGY   Oh my God! How did he get in?

CLEGG   You left the door wide open.

FOGGY   Get rid of him.

CLEGG   They're looking for him out there.

FOGGY   I'm not surprised. (*Sees* COMPO *about to eat
             something from the table, snarls.*) What's he
             got, that man?

             (FOGGY'S *snarl brings the* FLASHER *out
             apologetically from his hiding place.*)

FLASHER   Nothing special, bless your heart, I'd be the
             first to admit.

COMPO   (*with his mouth full*) It's just a morsel.

FLASHER   (*to* COMPO) I'd don't know that I'd quite go
             that far.

FOGGY   He'll have to go.

FLASHER   Agh wall. I suppose it's inevitable.

             (*The* FLASHER *puts on a hangdog expression
             and summons a brief but hacking cough
             from his very depths.*)

FLASHER   Thank you for your kindness.

             (*From his huge raincoat pocket he produces
             a pair of gloves which he begins to pull on
             rather fussily and delicately.*)

FLASHER   Thank you for a moment's warmth and
             shelter. Thank you for opening to me,
             however temporarily, the welcome of your
             fireside.

COMPO   What fireside?

CLEGG   Be quiet. You know what he means.

(CLEGG *is falling for the* FLASHER'S *plucking at the heart-strings.* FOGGY *is merely desperate to get rid of the man and is pacing nervously and groaning cynically just outside the* FLASHER'S *eyeline and trying to prevent* COMPO *from making further inroads into the goodies on the table.*)

FOGGY   Be sensible. Don't start weakening. We can't keep him here. Just give me one good reason for not throwing him out.

CLEGG   (*thinks desperately*) He hasn't finished his celery.

(FOGGY *groans. The* FLASHER *snatches another piece of celery, and taken a loud bite.* FOGGY *removes it from him and points him towards the door, right.*)

FOGGY   Out!

(*The* FLASHER *goes quietly.*)

FLASHER   (*despondently*) Well thanks anyway. You've been kindness itself. A little oasis of warmth.

(*He looks round the room and his chest heaves a huge sigh.*)

FLASHER   Think of me sometimes when I've gone.

CLEGG   I feel terrible now.

FOGGY   Out!

(*As* FOGGY *tries to propel the* FLASHER *through the door, the* FLASHER *gives him a loud kiss.*)

FLASHER   I'll be off then.

               (FOGGY *leaps back as if stung, wiping his
               cheek.*)

FLASHER   I know you must be wondering why does he
               run about the streets. Dressed only in two
               raincoats and a balaclava.

CLEGG   Two raincoats?

FLASHER   It gets bloody nippy in one.

COMPO   Tha's in the wrong profession if tha can't
               stand a bit a weather.

FOGGY   Why do you run about the streets dressed in
               only . . . ?

FLASHER   Advertising.

ALL THREE   Advertising?

FLASHER   You have to advertise. It's no good having a
               product if the public never sees it.

               (*Our three exchange an incredulous glance.
               The* FLASHER *reaches inside his huge
               raincoat.*)

FLASHER   Listen – Can I show you something?

               (*Our three hastily turn their backs and
               cover their eyes.*)

FLASHER   It won't take a minute.

               (*Our three advert their eyes even further.
               From inside his coats the* FLASHER
               *produces a slender telescopic device. He
               demonstrates it proudly.*)

FLASHER   I just know there'd be a demand for this if
             only I could bring it to the attention of the
             public.

             (*Our three clutch each other in disbelief.*)

FLASHER   But advertising is so expensive. You
             wouldn't believe how much Yorkshire
             Television wants to charge just to let me
             show it. For fifteen seconds at peak periods.

FOGGY   We've got to get him out of here.

CLEGG   I'll push him from the back. I don't mind
             pushing him from the back.

FLASHER   And let's be fair about this. Here I am
             covered from head to Hush Puppies in two
             chunky raincoats.

FOGGY   Keep quiet.

FLASHER   And it's me you're throwing out. (*He points
             to* COMPO.) Look at him.

             (*They all look at* COMPO *in his underpants.*)

FLASHER   That's Brand X if I ever saw one.

COMPO   Cheeky wap.

FOGGY   He can explain his condition.

FLASHER   I can explain my condition.

COMPO   Tha's a sex maniac.

             (*The* FLASHER *goes sulky and begins pacing
             about – deeply offended. They watch him
             nervously.*)

CLEGG   You've upset him.

COMPO   He wants upsetting.

FLASHER   I might have known you'd take that attitude.
                  Trust people to take that attitude.

FOGGY   What attitude are we supposed to take?

FLASHER   Where's your trust?

FOGGY   Where's your trousers?

FLASHER   Alright. Alright. All I ask is you keep an
                  open mind and have a look at this.

                  (*They turn away hastily.*)

FLASHER   My new improved Modesty Mark Two
                  Mechanical inside Leg Detector.

                  (*Intrigued, they peep cautiously and relax,
                  when they see he is flaunting nothing more
                  sinister than a telescopic cane.*)

FOGGY   Your what?

FLASHER   My Mechanical Inside Leg Detector Code
                  name MILD: 'M' for mechanical, 'I' for
                  inside, 'L' for leg, 'D' for detector. Spells
                  MILD. I call it my Modesty Mild. (*He
                  thrusts it at them.*) Here. Have a look. The
                  principle is quite simple. It's practically
                  maintenance-free. You merely grasp it by
                  the middle here.

                  (*He bends to demonstrate on* COMPO *who
                  clutches his knees together nervously.*)

COMPO   Get him off.

FLASHER   It won't hurt you.

COMPO   He's poking a stick up me leg.

FLASHER   You merely raise the upper section – thus.

COMPO   Careful. Careful.

FLASHER   Until some obstruction is encountered.

COMPO   Aagh!

FLASHER   Then holding the Modesty Mild in that
                 precise position . . .

COMPO   Don't anybody move.

FLASHER   The operator –

COMPO   Hey up! Tha's not operating on me. I don't
                 want The Operation.

                 (*By now more interested*, FOGGY *and* CLEGG
                 restrain COMPO.)

FOGGY   Relax.

COMPO   With that he's got on the end of his stick?

CLEGG   Try and think like a toffee apple.

FLASHER   The operator then allows the lower section
                 to descend to the floor – thus. And where it
                 comes to rest, the inside leg measurement
                 can then be easily read from the clearly
                 marked scale. Twenty eight and one half
                 inches.

                 (COMPO *breaks away*.)

FLASHER   Hang about. I haven't done you in metric.

COMPO   Bog off!

FOGGY

Twenty eight and one half inches. That's really quite ingenious.

COMPO

Poking sticks up people's legs.

FLASHER

Not only ingenious. And I must say with all modesty, unfailingly accurate. But the real essence of this little beauty, my major selling platform is, I feel, the Modesty Factor. We must never overlook the Modesty Factor.

CLEGG

Especially when we're running about with no trousers.

(*The* FLASHER *glares at* CLEGG.)

FLASHER

I can explain that.

CLEGG

I can explain that. You're crackers.

(*The three clutch each other nervously as the* FLASHER *goes storming about emotionally.*)

FLASHER

They always say that when you're different when you're pushing forward the frontiers of human experience.

COMPO

I can tell thee what he was pushing forward.

FLASHER

When you dedicate your life try developing something new.

COMPO

And chilly. Surprisingly chilly.

FLASHER

They said Galileo was crackers.

COMPO

Who?

FOGGY

Telescopes.

COMPO	(*nods*) Oh.
FLASHER	They said Alexander Graham Bell was crackers.
	(COMPO *looks at* FOGGY *for enlightentment.*)
FOGGY	Telephones.
CLEGG	The way mine works maybe he was crackers.
	(*They flinch as the* FLASHER *bears down on them.*)
FLASHER	You're wondering, aren't you, why I'm dressed like this.
COMPO	(*points to* CLEGG) No. He's wondering. Me. I'm not a big wonderer.
CLEGG	(*points to* FOGGY) If it's wondering you're after, I can recommend . . .
FOGGY	Just be careful where you're poking that damned implement.
COMPO	Now he tells him.
FLASHER	Well I'll tell you why I'm dressed like this.
	(*The* FLASHER *resumes his agitated pacing.*)
FLASHER	I'm dressed like this because the world has no imagination. Shows no appreciation.
COMPO	What's he want? Applause?
CLEGG	I should have thought people clapping their hands together is the last thing a flasher wants while he's working.

FLASHER   You spend the best years of your life on
               your invention. You finally get it right.
               And the world greets it with a big yawn of
               indifference.

COMPO   Same wi' my racing ferret. I bred this racing
               ferret. It could a caught on. I mean look
               how much smaller you could a built your
               racecourses.

               (*They flinch again as the* FLASHER *rears up
               at them.*)

FLASHER   You wouldn't believe the apathy there is
               out there when it comes to the inside leg. I
               called a Press Conference.

COMPO   I never thought a that.

FOGGY   Shut up about your damned ferrets.

FLASHER   I invited all the media.

               (*The* FLASHER *is pacing again agitatedly.*)

FLASHER   The National Dailies. The major Sundays.

COMPO   I could have had Red Rum. As a ferret.

               (COMPO *avoids a poke from* FOGGY.)

FLASHER   The local press. The trade journals. I even
               sent one to "Exchange and Mart".

FOGGY   "Exchange and Mart". I know the old
               "Exchange and Mart". (*He turns to* COMPO
               and CLEGG.) I once bought a reconditioned
               prismatic marching compass from the old
               "Exchange and Mart".

COMPO   Thee life's been full of incident, Foggy.

(He ducks a swing from FOGGY.)

FLASHER I booked a hall. I hired the main room of the St John's Ambulance hut.

CLEGG Wow! The main room of the St John's Ambulance hut.

COMPO Spares no expense this beggar, does he.

FOGGY I know the main room of the St John's Ambulance hut. That's the one with the big chart showing all the internal organs.

CLEGG *(wincing)* In living technicolour. I once went to a wedding reception there. I couldn't help thinking this is no place to be eating strawberry flan.

FLASHER I had leaflets printed. I had promotional material ready. I hired seventeen people of assorted leg size. I was offering practically the full range of civilized inside leg as we know it.

(Our three are quietly comparing their own leg sizes.)

FLASHER There they were at my use, seventeen assorted inside legs just waiting for the world's Press to apply my invention to them. *(He waves the device dramatically.)* My new, improved Modesty Mark Two Mechanical Inside Leg Detector. My Modesty Mild. Child of my imagination. The biggest historical advance in Public Decency since the Chastity Belt.

(He goes raging frustratedly around the room.)

COMPO Nora Batty has one.

FOGGY   Nora Batty has a Chastity Belt?

COMPO   A beauty. Everytime I threaten her chastity,
             she gives me a belt.

             (*The* FLASHER *darts towards* FOGGY *for a
             quick measure of his inside leg.* FOGGY *backs
             away.*)

FOGGY   What's he doing with that stick?

FLASHER   Stand still.

COMPO   Now tha knows how it feels.

FLASHER   You see. How modesty is maintained.

CLEGG   Looks unnatural to me. Foreign bodies up
             your inside leg.

FOGGY   Don't distract him. For God's sake if his
             hand slips.

FLASHER   You see. How the operator's hand remains
             at all times on the implement. None of
             this fumbling up your crutch that goes on
             to this very day in the world's tailoring
             establishments.

             (*Much to* FOGGY's *relief the* FLASHER *stands
             up and reads the instrument.*)

FLASHER   Thirty two and a half. Am I right?

FOGGY   He's right.

CLEGG   That's uncanny.

FOGGY   It certainly was for a moment.

FLASHER   And do you know how many came to my
                 Press Conference?

                 (*He suddenly seizes* FOGGY *by the shoulders
                 and begins shaking him violently.*)

FLASHER   Nobody. Zilch. Zero. Nobody came.

                 (COMPO *is cackling at* FOGGY'S *predicament
                 until the* FLASHER *leaves* FOGGY *and starts
                 the same on* COMPO.)

FLASHER   Nobody. Not even "Exchange and Mart". It
                 was so embarrassing. In the silence of that
                 lonely room just me and seventeen inside
                 legs.

CLEGG   Don't you mean thirty four?

                 (*The* FLASHER *releases* COMPO *and shakes*
                 CLEGG.)

FLASHER   I mean seventeen. It takes two to make an
                 inside leg.

                 (*He releases* CLEGG *and goes pacing again
                 frustratedly.*)

CLEGG   Sorry I spoke.

                 (CLEGG *straightens his tie and eases his stiff
                 collar.* FOGGY *restores order to his shoulder
                 pads.* COMPO *is listening to his elbow.*)

FOGGY   Feller's losing control.

CLEGG   Got me right in the elbow. I could hear me
                 elbow.

                 (*They hear the sound of furniture being
                 moved upstairs.*)

CLEGG   What are they doing in my bedroom?

FOGGY   Whatever it is they must be nearly finished.
                 We've got to get him out of here.

                 (*They look at the* FLASHER *who is stowing his
                 invention away despondently.*)

COMPO   I wonder how he works his lighting
                 arrangements.

FOGGY   Never you mind how he works his lighting
                 arrangements. Let's just get him outside.

FLASHER   Can you imagine how rejected you feel at
                 your Press Conference when nobody turns
                 up. Standing there with your invention
                 in your hand. Under the critical eye of
                 seventeen redundant inside legs.

CLEGG   Embarrasaing.

FLASHER   And humiliating.

FOGGY   That's no excuse for rushing about during
                 the hours of darkness flashing your
                 particulars.

FLASHER   You have to advertise.

FOGGY   Not everything.

FLASHER   I know what I'm doing.

COMPO   We all know what tha's doing.

FLASHER   If you wish to bring your product to the
                 attention of an indifferent public you have
                 to come up with something eye-catching.

(*The* FLASHER *whips open his coat. Our three reel back, averting their eyes.*)

ALL THREE   Waargh!

FLASHER   You have to use a little sex with your advertising. Everybody else does.

(*The* FLASHER *pursues them with his back to the audience and gives them another glimpse. They stagger back again.*)

FLASHER   You're not looking.

(*The* FLASHER *closes his coats and complains sulkily.*)

FLASHER   You go to endless trouble then people can't be bothered to look.

COMPO   By God! That's eye-catching alright.

FOGGY   It gives you quite a chill. It's worse than your first bayonet attack.

CLEGG   That reminds me. I don't think I put my milk bottle out.

FLASHER   (*loudly*) You didn't look. You just think you saw what you saw.

FOGGY   We know that we saw.

FLASHER   You didn't even read the slogan.

ALL THREE   Slogan?

FLASHER   There you go you see.

COMPO   Hey up! He's been writing on it.

FLASHER   Didn't you see the card?

                   (*The* FLASHER *waves his arms in disgust as
                   he paces.*)

FLASHER   You make a comprehensive study of
                   marketing techniques. You go for maximum
                   impact and they don't even read the card.

                   (*He pauses – struck by an idea.*)

FLASHER   Of course it's more effective in the dark.

                   (*He looks round for a light switch and
                   before they can stop him he plunges the
                   room into darkness.*)

FLASHER   You'll get the full benefit now.

FOGGY   Oh my God! He's going to be floodlit.

                   (*At the sound of* NORA'S *voice they all
                   freeze.*)

NORA   (*off*) I say! Are you going to come and look
                   at this bedroom or aren't you?

FLASHER   I didn't know you'd got ladies here.

FOGGY   Stop him. Before he lights up.

                   (*They make a rush for the* FLASHER *but are
                   stopped in their tracks by a great burst of
                   light as he wafts open his coat. They stagger
                   back rubbing their eyes. The light goes off
                   again as the* FLASHER *closes his coat.*)

FOGGY   Aagh!

COMPO   Ooh!

CLEGG	Waw!
FLASHER	Could you see it that time?
FOGGY	Shut up!
FLASHER	Well tell me dammit. Did you get the message of my advert?
COMPO	Makes your eyes water.
FLASHER	Tell me honestly. Did it make you want to rush out and buy my Inside Leg Detector?
CLEGG	We'll have one. Just keep your hand off your switch.
FLASHER	It works. It works.
NORA	(*off*) I don't know what they're doing down there.
FOGGY	She's coming down.
CLEGG	Put the light on.
FOGGY	No don't put the light on. Not while there's two fools here without trousers.
NORA	(*off*) Are you there? What are you doing down there?
FOGGY	Get the Flasher out the back way.
CLEGG	Suppose he lights up in your hand?
COMPO	I've got him.
CLEGG	That's me.
NORA	(*off*) I say! Your bedroom's ready.

(NORA *appers in shadow in the doorway,*
left.)

NORA   What are you doing in the dark?

                       (*Another burst of light which our three*
                       manage quickly to stifle. CONSTANCE *appears*
                       behind NORA.)

CONSTANCE   What are they doing?

NORA   There's a light keeps flickering. They must
                       be watching television.

CONSTANCE   What's on?

NORA   One of them horror pictures by the looks of
                       it.

                       (FOGGY *hastens to steer the women back*
                       upstairs.)

FOGGY   Right then ladies. Let's have a look at the
                       bedroom then.

CONSTANCE   He's very firm. Isn't he firm.

NORA   I'd like to know who he thinks he's shoving.

                       (*With the ladies gone,* CLEGG *switches on the*
                       light.)

NORA'S VOICE   We're not going back upstairs. We haven't
                       come here to spend all night upstairs. Mind
                       your heel in that loose stair carpet. Will you
                       stop shoving. Stand aside. We're coming
                       downstairs.

                       (COMPO *grabs the spare folds of his*
                       undergarment and exits rapidly right.)

COMPO	I'll be in the outside toilet.
CLEGG	What about me?
COMPO	Sorry. It's a single.

(CLEGG *doesn't know what to do with the*
FLASHER *or where to go himself. After a*
second's dithering hesitation, he crams the
FLASHER *back under the table. The women*
enter, left as CLEGG *is still bending having*
tucked the FLASHER *out of sight.*)

NORA	What's he bent down there for?
CLEGG	It's me back. Me back. It goes occasionally.

(*The women stare at* CLEGG *as he does*
a hunchbacked grotesquely bent walk in
support of his story – the women look at
each other. NORA *shrugs.*)

CLEGG	It'll be alright in a minute.

(FOGGY *grabs* CLEGG.)

FOGGY	Where are they?

(CLEGG *signals under cover of further*
lumbar problems.)

CLEGG	One under there. One in the outside toilet.
FOGGY	Oh my God. We've got to get the other out. I'll go and see if the streets are clear.

(FOGGY *exits right unnoticed by the ladies.*
CONSTANCE *pulls* NORA *to one side for a*
quiet word.)

CONSTANCE	Let's get out of here.

NORA   We've only just come.

CONSTANCE   They're weird.

NORA   They're not weird. Well not really weird.

                (*They look at* CLEGG *who is very conscious
                of their scepticism and so perhaps tends to
                overdo his contortions a bit.*)

CONSTANCE   They're not weird?

CLEGG   Soon as this red mist clears.

NORA   Try and think of it as eccentric.

CONSTANCE   (*heading for the door*) You call it what you
                like.

NORA   (*hauling her back*) I call it a chance to
                improve your matrimonial prospects.

CONSTANCE   I hardly know the man. I only came for
                supper.

NORA   That's another thing. I'm not leaving here
                without a bite to eat. Just settle yourself
                down, Our Connie. If you're as allergic to
                silly beggars what have you been doing with
                Gifford Bewmont all these years?

                (CLEGG *has spotted the carrier bag full of
                clothes which* COMPO *has left. It's quite near
                the ladies. As* CLEGG *makes a beeline for it,
                the ladies scatter before him nervously.*)

CONSTANCE   What's he doing now?

CLEGG   Back in a minute ladies. I must just go to
                the outside toilet.

(*They watch him exit, right, with the bag.*)

CONSTANCE   He takes an overnight bag to the toilet?

(NORA *wanders towards the table where she begins inspecting the food on offer.*)

NORA   It's not him you have to worry about. Your Mister Dewhirst seems more normal. Where is he? Look he's gone. Shy, you see. You're going to have to show more encouragement, Our Connie.

CONSTANCE   He's too old for me.

NORA   At your age nobody's too old for you. Let's face it, you've not had a lot of luck with the younger ones, have you?

(CONSTANCE *is offended by the turn of the conversation and so presents her aunt with a frigid back and is thus unable to see the* FLASHER'S *arm as it emerges from under the tablecloth with the obvious intention of measuring* NORA *with his invention.* NORA *too is unaware of it as she moves along the table selecting munchables and just managing to miss the* FLASHER'S *first strike.*)

NORA   And you're getting nowhere permanent with that Gifford Bewmont. Famous silly beggar. If he won't set a date it's time you sent him on his way.

CONSTANCE   I don't wish to talk about it.

NORA   Well I do.

(NORA *moves again and evades the* FLASHER'S *second strike. This time* NORA *moves to the far side of the table. The*

FLASHER'S *hand can be seen feeling empty*
space at the audience side of the table in its
search for the absent NORA.)

NORA

If you look on the bright side you'll find
Foggy Dewhirst to be tall and neatly dressed
and just the kind of ideal dozy wet you
could soon manoeuvre into Holy Wedlock.

(*At the sound of* NORA'S *voice from the far*
side of the table, the FLASHER *withdraws*
his hand and we can see his operations no
longer. But we can infer what he's up to
next, very clearly, by the change in NORA'S
voice halfway through her next speech
as she tries to contain the shock of being
goosed by someone under the table whom
she clearly assumes must be FOGGY.)

CONSTANCE

I dow't think Mister Dewhirst is terribly
interested in women.

NORA

Don't leap to conclusions. You shouldn't
– (*Gasps. Her voice up half an octave.*) –
dismiss people like that. (*She tries to quell*
her shock.) Mister Dewhirst may be shy
enough to take cover in some places but I
can assure you Mister Dewhirst is a damn
sight more interested in women than you're
giving him credit for.

CONSTANCE

I don't believe it.

NORA

He could surprise you.

(NORA *backs sway from the table. She peers*
down as well as she's able without giving
the game away to CONSTANCE.)

NORA

Mister Dewhirst could get arrested for how
interested he is in women.

CONSTANCE	What makes you say that?
NORA	Oh, call it a woman's intuition. (NORA *draws* CONSTANCE *to one side.*) It's what you need girl. To get you off your mother's back and your mind on something other than judging people solely by how well they keep the prongs of their forks clean.
CONSTANCE	I can't abide dirty forks.
NORA	Get yourself a man of strong passion imperfectly surpressed.
CONSTANCE	Aunty Nora!
NORA	That'll take your mind off the cutlery. (*Raising her voice for the benefit of the* FOGGY *she thinks is under the table.*) Mister Dewhirst would be ideal. (*Lowering her voice again.*) Besides, it's time your mother had a little place on her own. Not just for sentimental reasons but to allow unimpeded access to the gentleman you know only as Mister Singleton.
CONSTANCE	(*shocked*) The insurance man?
NORA	We all need a bit on one side for our retirement.
CONSTANCE	My Mother?
NORA	She knows what she's doing. He covers her more than handsomely for Third Party, Fire and Theft.
	(CONSTANCE *walks to the far side of the table to try and indicate her displeasure. She daintily selects an after dinner mint.*)

NORA   That's right. Stay over there. I wouldn't be
                at all surprised if, sooner than you think,
                Mister Dewhirst didn't give you some sign
                of the intensity of his feelings. Some little
                sign in the presense of her aunty which
                could surely then be safely interpreted as a
                kind of any man's declaration of his intents.

                (CONSTANCE *ignores her aunt primly as she
                picks bits of fluff from her teeth.*)

NORA   It must seem like forever she's been waiting
                to see her only daughter securely goosed. I
                mean married! In time you'll learn to make
                allowances girl, for any small eccentricities
                you might observe in the behaviour of the
                man you'll be proud to call your . . .

                (CONSTANCE *leaps a foot in the air and utters
                a piercing shriek.*)

CONSTANCE   Arrrrgh!

NORA   . . . Husband.

CONSTANCE   The dirty bugger.

                (CONSTANCE *exits rapidly through the door,
                right, with* NORA *following.*)

NORA   Think of it more as an inarticulate
                expression of affection. The clumsy
                proposal of an essentially shy person. A
                groping towards . . . on second thoughts,
                scrub that.

                (NORA *exits, right.* FOGGY *enters rapidly,
                left.*)

FOGGY   Who screamed? What's the matter?

(*He hears the ear-splitting toot of the bugle outside the door, left, and covers his ears.*)

FOGGY   Oh shut up!

(GIFFORD *enters, left, bugle at the ready.*)

GIFFORD   I heard a scream.

FOGGY   We all heard a scream. Stop making such a racket.

GIFFORD   Who was it?

FOGGY   I'm going to find out if you'll shut up.

(FOGGY *exits, right and returns backwards immediately under the onslaught of* CONSTANCE *and her handbag.*)

CONSTANCE   Take that.

GIFFORD   Constance.

CONSTANCE   Gifford. Arrest this brute.

FOGGY   What have I done? What have I done?

CONSTANCE   You know whet you did. (*She falls in* GIFFORD'S *arms.*) Oh Gifford.

GIFFORD   (*to* FOGGY) You filthy swine. (*Listens with growing intensity as* CONSTANCE *whispers in his ear.*) Groping a person's fiancée.

FOGGY   I did?

GIFFORD   (*pulling out his notebook*) There you are, he admits it.

(NORA *is leaning in the doorway, right.*)

NORA   Put your book away. Her aunty saw it all.
      A little love play. After all, they're getting
      married.

FOGGY /
GIFFORD   Married!

      (NORA *eyes* FOGGY *threateningly and
      indicates* GIFFORD's *book*.)

NORA   Or arrested.

      (FOGGY *gulps*. NORA *gives him a hug*.)

NORA   Welcome to the family.

      (CONSTANCE *breaks away from* GIFFORD *and
      takes* FOGGY's *arm*.)

CONSTANCE I think it's only fitting Gifford that you
      should be among the first to know.

      (GIFFORD *puts his book away with many
      a sulk and adjusts his bugle*. COMPO *and*
      CLEGG's *faces can be seen peering in the
      door, right*.)

CONSTANCE Don't take it so hard. Gifford. We can still
      be good friends.

      (*She follows the sulking* GIFFORD *out of the
      door, left, taking a thunderstruck, glassy-
      eyed zombie of a* FOGGY *with her*. NORA
      follows, smirking*.)

NORA   Mind you – not as good as you have been.

      (*They all exit, left*. CLEGG *enters, right*.)

CLEGG   Or dear! He's got himself engaged.

COMPO   (*off*) Silly beggar.

CLEGG   Well don't stand in the doorway. Come in.

COMPO   (*off*) Tha's sure there's nobody looking.

CLEGG   There's nobody looking.

                 (COMPO *enters sheepishly in his kilt.*)

CLEGG   How are we going to get him disengaged?

COMPO   Don't ask me. I've got me own troubles.

                 (CLEGG *exits, right. Alone on stage,* COMPO
                 *drifts towards the table. He pinches a crisp
                 and turns towards the audience. We see the*
                 FLASHER'S *hand emerge and next minute*
                 COMPO *shrieks as he is goosed.*)

FLASHER   Twenty seven and a half.

COMPO   You said that.

CLEGG   (*from the doorway.*) Get him upstairs!

COMPO   The bugger's just been upstairs.

CLEGG   We'll have to hide him up there till the
                 streets are clear.

                 (*They are helping the* FLASHER *to emerge
                 when* FOGGY *enters, left in a stunned
                 condition.*)

FLASHER   What's up with him?

COMPO   He's hearing wedding bells.

                 (FOGGY *groans long and pitifully.*)

                 Curtain. End of Act One.

ACT TWO

CLEGG's *dining room. The stage is empty but we can hear voices outside, left, calling their goodbyes.* NORA's *and* CONSTANCE's *voices sound catlike with pleasure.* FOGGY's *and* CLEGG's *responses are less cheerful. The table has been cleared of all its things and the cloth removed. The front door closes and* FOGGY *enters, left, still looking poleaxed. He comes to a halt and stares blankly into his bleak future.* CLEGG *enters, left.*

CLEGG	I thought they'd never go.
FOGGY	They haven't really gone, have they. They're going to come back. For me. One morning. Early. I'm going to be given the comforts of a priest. They they'll lead me out and stand me up against an altar.
	(FOGGY *pours himself a stiff drink.*)
CLEGG	Well you're the one who wanted a bit of female companionship.
FOGGY	Not forever.
CLEGG	Nothing's forever.
FOGGY	Oh that's great isn't it. You mean I've still got one thing to look forward to. Dropping dead.
CLEGG	Don't underestimate dropping dead. I've known some very canny people do it. There must be something in it.
FOGGY	Just because I don't wish to go that far you needn't think I'm resigned to wedlock. Maybe I can elope. On my own. Just one of me.

CLEGG	And live like a fugitive? While they just hunt you down?
FOGGY	Isn't there some organisation that can help people like me? What about those people who used to hide shot-down RAF men during the war?
CLEGG	They're all abroad somewhere.
FOGGY	I could go abroad.
CLEGG	I thought you liked the woman.
FOGGY	Who said I liked the woman?
CLEGG	You said you liked the woman.
FOGGY	I was exaggerating.

(CLEGG *has drifted towards the wall unit and is straightening a shelf when* FOGGY, *seized by an idea, grips* CLEGG *in fierce excitement, making* CLEGG *jump and another couple of shelves flop limply.*)

FOGGY	Maybe I can get the Flasher to confess.
CLEGG	I wish you wouldn't leap on people like that.
FOGGY	I don't leap on people. That's just the point. It's him, the cheeky beggar. And I'm taking the rap.
CLEGG	He's not going to give himself up, is he.
FOGGY	Why not? He'll only get probation. I'm going to get life.

CLEGG   It's not just probation. He'll get
         psychiatrists and social workers and you
         can't do that to anybody.

FOGGY   Meanwhile what am I supposed to do?

CLEGG   Just keep yourself pure for your bride.

FOGGY   It's not funny.

CLEGG   And leave off that stuff. You're not used to
         it.

FOGGY   I'm not used to getting married, either.

CLEGG   You're not wed yet. Relax. We'll think of
         something.

FOGGY   Oh that makes me feel better already.
         Coming from the idiot whose idea it was to
         hide the Flasher in the first place.

CLEGG   Well he needed hiding in the first place. And
         the second place and the third place.

FOGGY   Where is he?

CLEGG   Compo's still guarding him upstairs.

         (CLEGG *goes to the doorway, left, and calls
         upstairs.*)

CLEGG   You can come down now. They've gone.

FOGGY   Should I wear white, she says. Cheeky
         baggage. After fourteen years assorted
         colours with Gifford Bewmont.

         (FOGGY *pours another drink as the footsteps
         descend the stairs and* COMPO *enters, left,
         still pulling on the last of his own clothes.*)

COMPO	Hey up! Tha's no idea how good it feels to get thee legs back in trousers.
FOGGY	What about your charge?
COMPO	Well aye. Come to think of it. It's good to get that back in as well.
FOGGY	I'm talking about that idiot you're supposed to be watching upstairs.
COMPO	Oh don't worry about him. He's as good as gold.
FOGGY	Oh yes. We all know how well-behaved old Snake Fingers is.
CLEGG	Where have you left him?
COMPO	On the bed. He's sleeping like a baby. Well – when I say like a baby – you'll understand he's not got a lot in the way of a nappy on.
FOGGY	You've been peeping under those raincoats. He's been dying to have a squint under those raincoats.
COMPO	Well I wanted to read his advert. (*Winces at the memory.*) Makes you wonder how those signwriters keep their hands steady.
FOGGY	I don't know how that cheeky bugger can calmly go to sleep.
COMPO	He has some pills in his pocket. He swallowed a couple. Had a quick check to see if his battery was alright and he was away.
FOGGY	Charming.

(*As* FOGGY *gloomily swallows another drink,*
COMPO *slaps him cheerily on the back.*)

COMPO   And listen. Let me be among the first to
             congratulate . . .

FOGGY   Shut up!

             (COMPO'S *sustained, noisy barks of laughter
             drive* FOGGY *to take another drink as* COMPO
             *doubled with laughter, waddles about the
             place.*)

COMPO   Ooh – tha's dropped one this time, Foggy.

FOGGY   It's all a mistake.

COMPO   Aye. Thine.

             (COMPO *points the finger at the mortified*
             FOGGY *and waddles helplessly about.*)

COMPO   Talk about the Demond Lover. Hey up! Tha
             must be dynamite.

             (COMPO *leans weakly on* CLEGG, *who is
             having trouble suppressing his own giggles.*)

COMPO   What's tha want for a wedding present,
             Foggy?

FOGGY   It's not funny.

CLEGG   Now be reasonable. It is a bit funny.

FOGGY   Not from here.

             (FOGGY *pours another drink which* CLEGG
             hurriedly removes from him.)

CLEGG   And go easy. With that stuff. (*To* COMPO.)
               He's just had fourteen.

COMPO   There's no holding him tonight, is there.

FOGGY   (*rather precisely*) I am perfectly capable . . .

COMPO   Sees booze and women and he goes mad.

FOGGY   I am totally in command of all my falcuties.

COMPO   Of his what?

FOGGY   Falcuties, you ignoramus. Have you never
               heard of falculties?

CLEGG   Oh God! I told him to lay off. Help me
               get hm in a chair. He has that look certain
               people have when they're about to fall
               down.

               (CLEGG *steers* FOGGY *to a chair, lowers him
               down and begins patting* FOGGY'S *cheeks,
               and snapping fingers in front of* FOGGY'S
               eyes.)

CLEGG   Come on Foggy. You must be in there
               somewhere.

COMPO   Loosen his tie.

CLEGG   Look at his eyeballs. That's a terrible colour
               for eyeballs.

CLEGG   (*peering closely*) Don't panic. My Uncle
               Wilf's were that colour. Mind you he
               dropped dead one night.

               (*They both begin fanning* FOGGY *and patting
               his cheeks.*)

CLEGG	Wake him up!
COMPO	He's not asleep. His eyes are open.
CLEGG	You call that open? That's not open. That's just stuck between floors.
COMPO	Say something, Foggy.

(*They step back nervously as* FOGGY *rises slowly from his chair, his features stamped by an expression of awful melancholy. He drags out his words from some gloomy sepulchre deep within his being.*)

FOGGY	I can't get married. I'm not used to it.
CLEGG	We'll think of something, Foggy.

(CLEGG *is startled to find* FOGGY *gripping him by the throat.*)

FOGGY	When? When??
CLEGG	(*wriggling free*) Soon as I get me breath back.
FOGGY	Do you think I'm too old for the Foreign Legion?
COMPO	Tha's nearly too old for the British Legion.
CLEGG	Don't upset him. He'll have your throat.

(*They watch* FOGGY *moving about as if in a trance.*)

FOGGY	It costs money to get married. And I was saving mine for someone very dear to me.
COMPO	Who's that?

FOGGY   Me.

(FOGGY *pours another drink.* CLEGG *removes it from* FOGGY's *reach.*)

FOGGY   I'm essentially a loner. Especially in bed.

CLEGG   Listen. We'll deal with your problem when we've got rid of him upstairs – first things first. Let's get him out. I shall never get a wink of sleep if he's in the house.

(CLEGG *leads the way and they all exit, left.* FOGGY *a bit unsteadily.*)

CLEGG   I shall never dare close me eyes.

FOGGY   And how much sleep do you think I'm going to get? You've got to get me out of this. It makes you feel as if the bottom's dropped out of everything.

COMPO'S VOICE   Last time I climbed these stairs I was wearing a kilt. That makes thee feel as if the bottom's dropped out of everything.

(*They've gone too far to hear the knocking at the back door. It is repeated a few times, then we hear* GIFFORD's *voice calling from somewhere right.*)

GIFFORD'S VOICE   Dewhirst! Are you there, Dewhirst? Show your face, you sneaky ponce. It's me. Gifford Bewmont. Royal Signals. Come to challenge you, Dewhirst. I'm coming in. Where are you? Royal Engineers? Can you hear me, I've shot 'em.

(*He appears in the doorway, right, in civilian clothes, his Royal Signals blazer. He is swaying slightly. Bicycle clips on his grey flannels.*)

GIFFORD   Where's he gone, the sneaky twot. Where are you? What's he doing with her now? Where's he taken her?

               (*He enters the room unsteadily and makes a considerable balls of lighting a cigarette. He makes use of the lighted match to peer suspiciously under the table.*)

GIFFORD   Gone! (*Straightens up sadly and blows the match out after several inaccurate attempts.*) Gone! And with the woman I love. And have been loving approximately twice a week for these past many years. I've had my supplies cut by a sapper, the swine. All I've got in the world now is me Hercules bicycle.

               (*He looks around for somewhere to put the dead match. He can't find an ashtray. He lays the match carefully on a shelf of the wall unit, turns his back on it and the shelf collapses.*)

GIFFORD   Me Hercules bicycle. Propped outside without a lock or chain. That's all I need. Some thieving Herbert to have it away with me Hercules bicycle.

               (GIFFORD *exits, right.* CLEGG *enters, left, as if he's not quite sure he's heard someone.*)

COMPO'S VOICE Hey up Cleggy. Don't leave me wi' me hands full a Flasher.

CLEGG   Not so loud. I thought I heard somebody.

FOGGY'S VOICE   What am I doing standing here holding this dead person?

COMPO'S VOICE   He's not a dead person. He's just sleeping, that's all. He put himself to sleep. You remember.

FOGGY'S VOICE   The only thing I remember is I'm engaged to be married.

CLEGG   Keep him quiet.

(CLEGG *peers through the door, right, and then through the serving hatch. He shrugs. there are various grunts, bumps and noises coming from the stairs.* CLEGG *spies the latest collapsed shelf.*)

CLEGG   It's alright. It must have been this damned thing. Folding its petals for the night.

COMPO'S VOICE   Hurry up, Cleggy. We're dropping this slippery beggar.

CLEGG   I'm coming. Save me a leg. I don't want the Parson's Nose.

(*As* CLEGG *exits, left, and runs upstairs,* GIFFORD *enters, right, on his Hercules bicycle. He dismounts with great dignity, pats his trusty steed and props it carefully against the table.*)

GIFFORD   Now then. Where is he? Where are you, Constance? What's he done with her?

(*He hears some bumping and grunting from above.*)

GIFFORD   Upstairs already. My God, he's not wasting any time.

COMPO'S VOICE   Hey up! Has thy ever seen legs as bare as this?

FOGGY'S VOICE   Don't look at 'em. Lift 'em!

                (GIFFORD'S *eyes are popping from his head.*)

CLEGG'S VOICE   It's all very well but when they haven't got
                many clothes on, where are you supposed to
                get a grip?

GIFFORD   Oh my God! They're all up there. It's an
                orgy. And with my bint. It's no good, I can't
                listen to this.

CLEGG'S VOICE   Can we rest a minute on the banister?

FOGGY'S VOICE   Keep going while the going's good.

COMPO'S VOICE   We're never going to get round this corner if
                some butterfingers doesn't lift his end up a
                bit.

                (*It's all too much for* GIFFORD, *who exits,
                right, wailing and covering his ears. The
                noise from the staircase covers his exit and
                after more bumping and grunting* FOGGY,
                CLEGG *and* COMPO *enter, left, manhandling
                the limp but happily smiling* FLASHER *as he
                dangles unhelpfully between them.*)

FOGGY   It's incredible how limp a person can go.

CLEGG   Would you care to rephrase that?

FOGGY   Of course some idiot had to let him take a
                sleeping pill.

COMPO   How can I stop him taking pills? They're his
                pills.

CLEGG   We'll get some coffee down him.

(*They all come to a confused halt as they see the bicycle.* CLEGG *can't yet see it because his back's to it.*)

CLEGG   What have you stopped for?

FOGGY   There's a bicycle.

CLEGG   What do you mean there's a bicycle? We're not crossing the street.

FOGGY   There is a bicycle.

(CLEGG *gapes at the machine. They prop the* FLASHER *in a chair. He begins to fall. They get him to his discoordinated feet again and stretch him out. He sighs peacefully. They circle the bicycle.*)

CLEGG   It is a bicycle.

COMPO   That's true.

FOGGY   We can see it's a bicycle. Where's it from?

CLEGG   I believe a lot of 'em are made in Nottingham.

FOGGY   How did it get here?

(*They consider the probabilities.* COMPO *has a look through the door, right, and returns shaking his head.* FOGGY *has a secretive peep through the serving hatch and returns shaking his head. They regroup in a huddle, exchanging perplexed glances, unaware that behind them the* FLASHER *is stretching lazily. His head comes in contact with the handlebars. He rings the bell, startling the little group out of their wits. They dive for the* FLASHER *and detach him from the machine.* FOGGY *downs another drink.*)

FOGGY   We'll have to keep him quiet.

CLEGG   Never mind quiet. Just make sure his coats stay fastened.

COMPO   Has tha' see these front forks?

CLEGG   I'd rather not if it's all the same to you.

FOGGY   Open your eyes. He means the bicycle. And he's got a point.

CLEGG   Would you care to rephrase that as well?

COMPO   I've seen this machine before.

FOGGY   *Exactly.* Massive front forks, a sturdy frame. It's Gifford Bewmont's endurance bicycle. He's round here somewhere. Sneaky beggar. Just what we need when we're trying to get this lunatic back out on the street.

CLEGG   I thought I heard somebody downstairs.

COMPO   We he can't have come in the front door, we'd have heard him upstairs.

FOGGY   The back way. I'll go and have a look out the back way. Keep the Sleeping Beauty quiet.

            (FOGGY *exits, right, swaying a little as he goes.*)

CLEGG   He looks quiet enough at the moment.

(COMPO *and* CLEGG *are gathered round the table, looking down on the contentedly snoozing* FLASHER.)

COMPO He's got a big enough grin on his dial. His dreams can't be bad.

CLEGG Advertising! (CLEGG *chuckles.*) I like his nerve.

(*They panic a bit about how to conceal the* FLASHER *as they hear raised voices through the door, right.*)

FOGGY'S VOICE You can't come through here.

GIFFORD'S VOICE Stand aside. Me bike's in there.

FOGGY'S VOICE Well it shouldn't be in there. Sit down, man. You can hardly stand.

GIFFORD'S VOICE Listen who's talking. You don't look so steady yourself. Out the way! There's no ex-tulip from the Royal Engineers coming between me and my Hercules bicycle.

FOGGY'S VOICE When I said sit down I didn't necessarily mean on the floor. However – please yourself.

(FOGGY *appears in the doorway, right, making signals to* CLEGG *and* COMPO.)

FOGGY It's Gifford Bewmont. Drunk as a skunk. Get the Sleeping Beauty out of here.

CLEGG Oh not upstairs again!

FOGGY No. Get rid of him altogether.

(GIFFORD'S *voice draws* FOGGY *away again.*)

GIFFORD'S VOICE   Where's he gone? I'm here to challenge you, Dewhirst. We'll see who's the best man.

(FOGGY *blocks* GIFFORD'S *attempt to enter, right, and pushes him back into the living room.*)

FOGGY   Will you get back in there and let's discuss this calmly. Being the best man's as close as I ever intended to get to a wedding.

GIFFORD   Look after her, Dewhirst. She's only a child.

FOGGY   She's nearly forty if she's a day.

(*As* FOGGY *succeeds in pushing* GIFFORD *into the living room,* COMPO *and* CLEGG *are manhandling the beaming and quite contented* FLASHER, *who plants a kiss in the course of their struggles on* COMPO'S *face.*)

COMPO   Get him off.

CLEGG   Less noise. He won't hurt you.

COMPO   No? He didn't do me any good when I were wearing that kilt.

(*With a lot of difficulty they begin half-walking the over-pliable* FLASHER *towards the door, left.*)

CLEGG   Oh Lord! Don't let his raincoats come open right now.

(*As they approach the door, the sound of the front door bell freezes them in their tracks.*)

CLEGG   Now what?

COMPO   Get him upstairs again.

CLEGG   We can't. Whoever's at the door's going to see us through the glass.

                 (*They shuffle and twist in an agony of indecision for a moment.* GIFFORD'S *voice booms drunkenly.*)

GIFFORD'S VOICE What do you mean you've no bicycle? What kind of a man are you? Don't answer that. I heard you upstairs without your bicycle. You swine.

                 (*The front doorbell rings again.*)

COMPO   The serving hatch.

CLEGG   What?

COMPO   Shove him through the serving hatch.

CLEGG   Will he go?

COMPO   He'll have to flaming go.

                 (*They manoeuvre the still amiably grinning* FLASHER *towards the hatch.* FOGGY *appears momentarily in the doorway, right.*)

FOGGY   Get rid of him.

COMPO   We're trying to get rid of him.

FOGGY   I'll try and keep this other idiot occupied.

                 (FOGGY *exits again,* COMPO *and* CLEGG *shove the* FLASHER'S *head through the hatch and begin trying to hoist the rest of him through.*)

COMPO   Are you shoving?

CLEGG   I'm shoving. I'm just trying hard not to
                     think about what I'm shoving against.

                     (*The doorbell begins to ring more
                     insistently.*)

COMPO   Fetch a chair. He can use it for a step.

                     (CLEGG *nips to the door, left, and calls out to
                     the person ringing the bell.*)

CLEGG   Just a minute. Be with you in a minute.

                     (CLEGG *grabs a dining room chair and they
                     are able to assist the wobbly-legged* FLASHER
                     *onto it. They get his head and shoulders
                     through together with his knees.*)

CLEGG   Oh God he's stuck. It's them two raincoats.

COMPO   Now what?

CLEGG   He'll have to stay there while I answer the
                     door and get rid of whoever it is.

                     (*They make final adjustments to the*
                     FLASHER'S *raincoats and leave him wedged
                     in the serving hatch with his covered
                     rear bulging a little into the dining
                     room.* CLEGG *hurries to answer the door,
                     left. He takes a final, fearful look at the*
                     FLASHER'S *appearance then exits, left. We
                     hear the door being opened.* COMPO *stands
                     deliberately in front of the serving hatch.*
                     NORA *enters, left, followed by* CLEGG.
                     She stares warily at COMPO, *who smiles
                     innocently.*)

NORA   Nearly half-way home when I realised I'd
                     left me umbrella.

CLEGG   We'll find your umbrella, Nora. (*Tries to steer her away.*) You just rest yourself.

NORA   I know what you mean. It's been one of those evenings you'll always remember.

CLEGG   Oh it has. It has.

NORA   Our Connie's still in a kind of daze, bless her. I sent her home to let the cat out. It's been good company for her, that cat. It's had to be. She picks such dozy men.

               (NORA *stares at* COMPO, *who is grinning nervously as he attempts to keep himself between* NORA *and the serving hatch.*)

NORA   What's he doing grinning like that?

COMPO   How do, Nora.

CLEGG   Well I can't see your brolly in here. Maybe you left it in the living room.

               (CLEGG *tries to steer* NORA *through the door, right, but she's not having any.*)

NORA   I could have sworn I had it in here.

               (NORA *is becoming conscious of something odd about* COMPO's *small circuit of movement as he tries to keep blocking her view of the serving hatch. She's also less than impressed by his poor response to her hints for getting a good brolly-search underway. She tries to encourage him a bit.*)

NORA   (*to* COMPO) Me umbrella. You could show some interest.

(COMPO *nods and continues to smile vacantly.* NORA *moves, he moves.*)

NORA   (*to* COMPO) A small, black, ladies' umbrella.

                (*He nods and smiles again.* NORA *shakes her head in disgust and has a word about* COMPO *with* CLEGG.)

NORA   He's not related to Harpo Marx or something, is he?

CLEGG   He's got a lot on his mind, Nora.

COMPO   I have. I have.

                (GIFFORD'S *voice booms suddenly from the living room.*)

GIFFORD'S VOICE Don't back out of it now, you sneaky stealer of a bloke's bint. I'm challenging you.

NORA   Gifford Bewmont! What's he doing here?

CLEGG   Come to challenge Foggy for the hand of your niece.

NORA   He's been after more than her hand. He's had his opportunity. I'm not having him coming here interfering with her more genuine prospects.

                (NORA *stalks determinedly through the door, right.* CLEGG *and* COMPO *check the condition of the* FLASHER.)

CLEGG   You could have said something to her. She was getting suspicious.

COMPO   It's not easy making small talk under these conditions. Is he still asleep?

CLEGG   Well he appears to be at this end. Mind you,
                     it's not all that easy to tell at this end.

                     (*They are startled by powerful noises from
                     the living room. The combined voices of*
                     FOGGY *and* GIFFORD *are raised in military
                     chant.*

FOGGY / GIFFORD
VOICES   One – two, three. One – two, three. One.
                     (*These chants are accompanied by the crash
                     of parade ground feet.*)

COMPO   Now what?

CLEGG   God knows. Do you think we could get rid
                     of this one while they're doing whatever
                     they're doing in there?

GIFFORD'S VOICE Move to the left in threes.

FOGGY'S VOICE   One – two, three. One – two, three. One.

                     (COMPO *and* CLEGG *reach for a secure grip
                     on the* FLASHER *but have to spin round
                     quickly and hide things with their bodies as*
                     NORA *re-appears in the doorway, right.*)

NORA   Men! How much varnish have these two
                     lunatics been drinking?

FOGGY'S VOICE   Squad! Squad will move to the right in
                     threes. Right incline.

GIFFORD'S VOICE One – two, three. One – two, three. One.

CLEGG   What are they doing?

NORA   A drill competition. At this time of night
                     would you believe. Army drill.

FOGGY'S VOICE   You call that a right incline you wobbly horrible creature. Look at you. Swaying like a daffodil.

GIFFORD'S VOICE   Swaying? That's not swaying. That's the rhythmic breathing of a powerful military rib cage. I'll give you swaying. Cheeky poof!

NORA   Well don't stand there. Can't you stop 'em?

CLEGG   Let 'em move about a bit. It might sober 'em up.

NORA   I'll sober 'em up.

(NORA *gives* CLEGG *and* COMPO *a frustrated glare and goes back into the living room. As soon as she's gone, they turn back to the* FLASHER. *They lay hands upon him.* FOGGY *enters, right, unobserved.*)

FOGGY   A rifle.

(*His voice makes* CLEGG *and* COMPO *jump guiltily.*)

CLEGG   Damn it all, Foggy. Do you have to come creeping in like that?

FOGGY   I'm looking for a rifle.

COMPO   Hey up! I don't like him either. But you can't go round shooting the bugger.

FOGGY   Rifles are not for shooting with. Rifles are for drilling with.

(FOGGY *goes poking about, searching.*)

FOGGY	I'm looking for something that feels like a rifle. Something I can drill with. I'll show that Tinkerbell from Royal Signals.

(CLEGG *takes another grip of the* FLASHER.)

CLEGG	Give us a hand with this.
FOGGY	I can't drill with that. I want something longer and thinner.

(COMPO *and* CLEGG *shake their heads in despair.*)

FOGGY	Incidentally, well done you men. Tell me, where did you get rid of the Flasher?
COMPO	We didn't. He's here.
FOGGY	Where?
COMPO	Here. This is him.
FOGGY	Good God! Where's his head?
CLEGG	In the kitchen.
FOGGY	Oh my God! How did that come *off*?
COMPO	It didn't come off. It's at the other end.
CLEGG	So get off back through there and keep Nora busy while we do something with him.

(*In a panic now,* FOGGY *hurries back into the living room. His exit is further speeded by the* FLASHER'S *loud but contented yawn.*)

FOGGY	Can't you keep him quiet?
COMPO	How? He's not yawning at this end.

(COMPO *and* CLEGG *reach once more for their burden when* GIFFORD *enters, swaying but taking elaborate countermeasures to correct it.* NORA *is about to follow him but* FOGGY *persuades her back into the living room.*)

FOGGY Come and have a sit down, Nora. The best chairs are in here.

NORA He wants to talk about the wedding, bless him.

(*She gives* FOGGY *a kiss. He gives a last despairing glance for* CLEGG *and* COMPO *as he leads* NORA *away.*)

COMPO Hey up! He's kissing my bird. Did tha see him kissing my bird?

GIFFORD Swaying! I'll give him swaying. Do I look as if I'm swaying to you?

(GIFFORD *tries to demonstrate his steadiness by standing to attention. He begins to topple like a felled tree.* COMPO *and* CLEGG *have to rush to steady this.*)

GIFFORD That's not swaying. That's more your temporary loss of balance due to the emotional upset of having some poofter from the Royal Nancy Engineers making it away with your bint. (*He stands, blinking owlishly at the* FLASHER'S *raincoat-draped rear.*) What's this?

CLEGG Why don't you go back in there and have a lie down, Gifford.

GIFFORD What the hell is this?

COMPO	Take thee bicycle, Gifford. Go give it a clean.
GIFFORD	I've never seen anything like it.
CLEGG	There's not many about?
GIFFORD	What is it?
CLEGG	(*to* COMPO) It's nothing really, Gifford. It's just your ordinary everyday – tell him.
COMPO	Tell him what?
CLEGG	What sort of everyday thing it might possibly be.
COMPO	Thee tell him.
GIFFORD	Somebody tell him.
CLEGG	It's nothing, Gifford. It's just a . . .
GIFFORD	Just a what?
CLEGG	A picture. That's it. It's a picture, you see. There's a frame round it. It's a sort of three-dimensional art.
GIFFORD	What's these things hanging down?
CLEGG	Covers! We have to cover it, you see. You don't want too much light on it.
COMPO	That's true.
CLEGG	Else the colours start to fade.

(*They are steering* GIFFORD *towards the living room door, right.*)

GIFFORD   Valuable, is it?

COMPO   Well – there'd be a ripply of interest if it
                ever came up in an auction room.

                (*They shove* GIFFORD *through the door and
                close it. They pause to mop their brows. The*
                FLASHER *yawns loudly.*)

CLEGG   I think he's coming round.

COMPO   Be back in a minute.

                (COMPO *exits quickly, left, and out through
                the front door.*)

CLEGG   Where are you going? Don't run out on
                me now. Don't forget who lent you a dress
                when you had no trousers on.

GIFFORD'S VOICE One – two, three. One – two, three. One.
                You diabolical, sloppy shower. You call that
                the posture of attention. What kind of shape
                is that for a wedding night?

                (NORA *appears in the doorway, right.*)

NORA   Do something. They're starting to fight.

                (CLEGG *hurries through as the best way
                of distracting* NORA's *attention from
                the* FLASHER. COMPO *enters, left, with a
                wheelbarrow.* CLEGG *re-enters, right.*)

NORA   What are you doing through there? Give us
                a hand.

                (*He makes it plain, by gesture, that he wants
                the* FLASHER *in the wheelbarrow.*)

CLEGG   She said *they* were fighting. They're not fighting. They're just sort of leaning on each other.

                 (NORA *re-enters.*)

NORA   Will you come and referee in here. They're getting their jackets off now for unarmed combat. What's he doing with a wheelbarrow?

                 (*From the living room comes the sound of* FOGGY *and* GIFFORD *making karate noises.*)

CLEGG   (*points to living room*) There's so much bull flying about through there. Don't you think we're going to need a wheelbarrow?

                 (*As the karate noises grow in splendour,* NORA *grits her jaw and exits again, right.*)

NORA   Just listen to 'em. This has gone far enough.

COMPO   Shut that door and let's get Trouserless Thomas in this barrow.

                 (CLEGG *closes the door, right, cutting off the karate grunts and bumps. He joins* COMPO *at the serving hatch. They begin tugging at the* FLASHER.)

COMPO   Pull

CLEGG   I'm pulling.

                 (*They hear a howl of agony from* GIFFORD.)

COMPO   He's stuck. We'll have to go round to the kitchen and shove till we can loosen him a bit.

*(COMPO and CLEGG exit, right. Their
opening of the door releasing more karate
noises. They close the door again. It opens
almost immediately and GIFFORD squirms
in, holding his crotch tenderly. His face is
contorted in pain and he walks very oddly,
trying to keep his knees together.)*

GIFFORD   Kee-rist! What a place to catch anybody. Oh
               dear. It makes your eyes water.

               *(He tries to walk off the pain. His little
               dance of agony eventually brings him to the
               serving hatch. He stares thoughtfully at the
               shape wedged in it.)*

GIFFORD   What kind of picture?

               *(He looks round to make sure he's
               unobserved then lifts up the dangling
               raincoats for a peek inside. He drops
               them hurriedly and backs off, thoroughly
               shocked.)*

GIFFORD   Man – that's some picture! Wow! I've seen a
               few still lifes – but . . . waagh!

               *(He totters to the door, right, weakly,
               shaking his head in disbelief.)*

GIFFORD   Who would ever believe they'd put a frame
               round that?

               *(He backs away for the door cautiously,
               protecting his crotch as COMPO and CLEGG
               enter.)*

CLEGG   What are you doing in here, Gifford?

GIFFORD   Mind who you're walking into. I've had one
               low blow already.

(*They begin shoving* GIFFORD *back into the living room.*)

CLEGG
Well don't throw thee towel in yet, Gifford. Get off back in there. Show him who's gaffer.

GIFFORD
Him? The Sugar Plum Fairy? It wasn't him who hit me low. It was Nora.

(*They shove him through the door and close it. They dive for the* FLASHER *and begin hauling him out from the serving hatch. An operation they perform with much grunting and straining.* COMPO *finds himself underneath the* FLASHER.)

COMPO
Get him off me. Get him off.

CLEGG
You're alright. He's asleep.

COMPO
Just get me out before he wakes up.

CLEGG
Don't panic.

(COMPO *manages to reverse the situation to* CLEGG'S *disadvantage.*)

COMPO
Who's in a panic?

(*They get the* FLASHER *into the wheelbarrow, they arrange his raincoats. He sits there mumbling peaceably, and wearing an amiable grin. As* CLEGG *leans over him, the* FLASHER *plants a friendly kiss on* CLEGG'S *cheek.* CLEGG *leaps back, startled.* COMPO *chuckles wickedly.*)

CLEGG
Never mind giggling. Come on. Let's get him out of here.

(They put the balaclava on the FLASHER *and begin wheeling him towards the door, left.)*

COMPO   I think his weight's all at one end.

CLEGG   Listen. After all we've been through with him, I'm well aware which end all his weight's at.

*(*CLEGG *opens the door, left, and they are going nicely when a great blare of bugle blowing from outside the front door stops them in their tracks.)*

COMPO   Oh God! Now what? What's he doing out there?

*(*FOGGY *enters, right, closing the door after him. He peers through the serving hatch and summons a ghastly smile for* NORA'S *benefit.)*

FOGGY   Two sugars in mine, Nora.

(He slams shut the hatch and holds it shut as he mops his brow weakly. Another bugle fanfare.)

GIFFORD'S VOICE Come out here, Dewhirst. Where are you? Let's see you get your lips round this. You've played enough tunes on me sweetheart.

(More bugle squawks.)

CLEGG   What did you let Gifford Bewmont go outside again for?

FOGGY   I couldn't stop him. Great dozy clown. He's gone out there to challenge me to a bugle competition.

COMPO	Can we wheel this idiot out the back way?
FOGGY	You can't. Nora's in the kitchen making strong black coffee. She'll see you.

(*The* FLASHER *stretches and yawns.*) |
FOGGY	(*to* FLASHER) Oh shut up!
CLEGG	We need a decoy. Somebody to lure Gifford Bewmont away.
FOGGY	What sort of decoy?
CLEGG	Somebody who thinks he is the Flasher.

(CLEGG *nudges* COMPO *and points to* FOGGY.) |
| CLEGG | Somebody the same height and build as the Flasher.

(FOGGY *begins shaking his head.*) |
FOGGY	No.
CLEGG	Somebody wearing one of the Flasher's raincoats.
COMPO	(*enjoying it*) And a balaclava.
CLEGG	I've got one upstairs. It keeps your ears warm lovely.
FOGGY	Definitely no.
COMPO	Tha can keep thee trousers on.
FOGGY	Suppose they caught me. How's that going to look in The Alvis Owner's Club?
COMPO	Tha's never owned a motor car.

FOGGY   I've got a radiator badge and workshop
                   manual.

CLEGG   So what if they do catch you? They can't
                   arrest you for wearing a raincoat and
                   balaclava. Especially when you've got all
                   the rest of your clothes on. All you've got
                   to do is draw them away from here. (*Nudges*
                   COMPO.) I mean we'd do it, wouldn't we. If
                   we were tall enough.

CLEGG   (*grinning*) Course we would. If we were tall
                   enough.

                   (CLEGG *and* COMPO, *both grinning, make*
                   themselves even smaller by bending their
                   knees.)

FOGGY   No.

                   (COMPO *and* CLEGG *begin peeling one of the*
                   raincoats from the the FLASHER. *Another*
                   burst of bugling from outside.)

COMPO   Just listen to that silly beggar. Loses his
                   bird so he tries to blow his brains out.

FOGGY   Don't say things like that.

COMPO   What? Blowing his brains out?

FOGGY   No. Losing his bird. He hasn't lost her. He
                   can have her back.

                   (*They advance on* FOGGY *with the raincoat.*)

FOGGY   No.

CLEGG   Come on, Foggy. You'll be putting one over
                   Gifford Bewmont.

COMPO	Tha reckons to have had all this army training. How to become a shadow. How to melt into the background.
FOGGY	I'm not saying I couldn't do it.
COMPO	How to move as silent as a finger up a nostril.
FOGGY	As silent as a phantom if you don't mind.
CLEGG	We ask you to do this one little thing, Foggy.
FOGGY	Little thing?
COMPO	I'm not surprised but tha dunt actually have to show it.
CLEGG	A favour for your friends, Foggy. The same likeable, stubborn pair you're going to be relying on to help you retain your bachelor status.
	(FOGGY *takes the hint and gives in reluctantly, allowing them to dress him in the raincoat.*)
FOGGY	I don't like it.
CLEGG	It won't hurt a bit.
FOGGY	This thing's still warm.
COMPO	He's a natural. He looks like a flasher already.
FOGGY	Shut up!
CLEGG	I'll go and get the balaclava. Fasten him up.

(*As* CLEGG *exits, left, another burst of bugle from outdoors.*)

GIFFORD'S VOICE   Where are you, Dewhirst? Where is he, the long prong? I'm waiting, Dewhirst.

FOGGY   Mouthy lot, the Royal Signals.

(*As the serving hatch opens,* COMPO *shoves* FOGGY *down out of sight as* NORA'S *head appears.*)

NORA   Do you want your coffee in . . .

(*She gapes at the* FLASHER *in the wheelbarrow.*)

NORA   What the hell is that?

(NORA *closes the hatch,* COMPO *shoves* FOGGY *towards the door, left.*)

COMPO   Get upstairs. Get upstairs. (*To* FLASHER.) And thee sit still. Don't move.

(FOGGY *exits, left, hurriedly as another burst of bugle from outside.* COMPO *prepares to intercept and distract* NORA *as she enters, right.*)

NORA   Who the devil have you got in the wheelbarrow?

COMPO   Oh Nora. At last we're alone.

NORA   Get off, you dozy clown.

COMPO   Oh Nora, I've been waiting for this.

NORA   (*she raises a fist*) You'll get some of this. Keep your eyes off me legs. He's always looking at me legs.

COMPO	Come in the living room. I've got something to show thee.
NORA	I'm not falling for that one. I haven't fallen for that one since I was seventeen. Mind you, I can remember it as if it was yesterday.
COMPO	Oh Nora! I love thee in this blouse.
NORA	Never mind oh Nora! Will you take your hand out the back of me blouse.
COMPO	I've lost all control of it, Nora. It sort of shot in there on its own, you bonny creature.
NORA	Get it out.
COMPO	Now, Nora. Don't have thee knee about in that threatening manner.
NORA	I'm warning you. You're only inches away from a nasty whack in the whatsits. Get your hand out.
COMPO	I'm trying to get it out. I've got me wristwatch fast in thee brassiere strap.
NORA	You dozy clown. Don't pull it. Don't pull it. You'll tear something.
COMPO	Put that knee down, Nora. Tha'll be doing a bit of damage theeself.
	(*They are now involved in a complicated tangle with* COMPO'S *hand jammed high up the back of* NORA'S *blouse.*)
NORA	Can't you wriggle it free?
COMPO	I'll try.

NORA   Don't make a meal of it. You don't have to
                    wriggle in that direction. Kindly wriggle in
                    the other direction.

COMPO   Listen. Whose wriggle is this?

NORA   Get on with it.

                    (*Their contortions are becoming more and
                    more complicated.*)

COMPO   Is there anything I could unfasten?

NORA   No there isn't. You can scrub that idea for a
                    start.

COMPO   We could be here for quite a while then,
                    love.

NORA   Just stand still. Don't move. You keep your
                    hand still. I'll wriggle.

                    (*She begins to sway and wave her body in
                    an attempt to free his hand. He watches with
                    undisguised admiration.*)

COMPO   Oh I like that.

NORA   Shut up!

COMPO   Oh I do like that. Hey up, Nora. Tha's just
                    like Yvonne De Carlo doing a belly dance.
                    (*He grunts in pain.*) Now Nora. That wasn't
                    in the choreography.

NORA   Is your hand out?

COMPO   No, but tha's made me eyes pop out a bit.

NORA   I can't go through life with you in me
                    blouse. Twist your wrist or something.

COMPO   It's no good, Nora. We're going to have to either get married or undo something.

NORA   Oh God! What got into you? What were you doing?

COMPO   It went to me head. Just thee and me alone.

NORA   How can we be alone with some beggar in a wheelbarrow?

COMPO   There's nobody in a wheelbarrow. Who's going to be in a wheelbarrow?

NORA   If I can ever get you from under my bra that's what I intend to find out.

COMPO   Forget the wheelbarrow. It's just a guy.

NORA   I can see that. But which guy?

COMPO   A guy for Bonfire Night. Fireworks and things. Penny for the Guy.

NORA   At this time of year?

COMPO   You have to be swift else the kids have cornered the market.

         (*Their struggles to be free have taken them near the wheelbarrow.*)

COMPO   Will tha stop pulling, Nora. Can tha bend down a bit? Let me see if I can . . .

         (NORA *obliges with her back to the wheelbarrow and* COMPO *is horrified to see the* FLASHER'S *hand sneak out and whip his measuring stick up* NORA'S *skirt. She shrieks and begins clobbering* COMPO.)

NORA   You cheeky swine.

COMPO   Will tha pack it in, Nora. I nearly had it
            there.

NORA   Don't I know it.

COMPO   Listen, Nora. We're going to have to undo a
            few things here.

NORA   Oh no you don't. Not with the lights on,
            anyroad.

            (*She hauls* COMPO *towards the light switch.*)

NORA   And I'll unfasten what needs to be
            unfastened. You just keep still.

            (*She switches off the lights. With the
            stage lights in darkness now their voices
            continue.*)

COMPO   If tha needs any help, Nora.

NORA   I don't. Just you keep still. Now keep your
            eyes closed and your hand still. Let me get
            this hook.

COMPO   We ought to come here more often.

NORA   Shut up!

COMPO   There's no two ways about it. If a bloke's
            got to get fast, this is the place.

NORA   Will you stop breathing in me ear.

COMPO   I can't help it, Nora. I'm full of admiration
            for what's happening under me nose.

NORA	Alright. It's undone. Now keep your eyes closed.
COMPO	Tha must be joking. Phwaw Nora! Tha wants to let that lot go more often. Surprising what a difference it makes.
NORA	Never mind about that. Can you get your watch untangled now?
COMPO	Me watch? It's been untangled for the last two minutes.
	(The sound of a slap.)
COMPO	I hadn't the heart to stop thee.
NORA	Don't put that light on yet.
COMPO	Give us a shout when tha's ready.
NORA	I'm never going to be ready if you don't take your hand away.
COMPO	It is away.
NORA	I know when it's away and when it's not away. *(She gasps.)* You cheeky monkey!
COMPO	Oh God. I know who it is. It's him again.
NORA	Just pack it in. I'm warning you. Are you thick?
COMPO	It's not as easy for me as you think.
NORA	What are you doing? Put me down. I don't want to sit on your knee. You great fool. It's a good job you've got more than your kilt on. My God! He hasn't got more than his kilt on.

COMPO   Er – Nora. I think there's something I ought
                to tell thee, Nora.

NORA   Will you let me off those damn boney knees.

COMPO   Go steady, Nora. That's not necessarily the
                kilt tha thinks it is. And don't for God's
                sake go prying into what a Scotsman wears
                underneath.

                (NORA *shrieks.*)

COMPO   I warned thee, Nora.

                (NORA *shrieks again. An answering burst of
                bugle and* GIFFORD *charges in to the rescue.*)

COMPO   Oh bloody hell! Come in, why don't you.

GIFFORD   A female under attack. They're at it again.
                Have no fear. The Bewmonts are here.

                (*He comes blundering into the furniture as
                he enters, left.*)

GIFFORD   In the dark, the swines.

NORA   Switch on the light. I'm sitting on some
                unknown knees. Oh God! Whose knees am I
                on?

GIFFORD   Have no fear.

NORA   Oh shut up, you fool and put the light on.

                (*After a bit more blundering into furniture,*
                GIFFORD *switches the light on.* COMPO *is
                covering his eyes.* NORA *stares in horror at
                the balaclava-covered features of the person
                she is sitting on. She shrieks again and
                jumps to her feet. The* FLASHER *gets to his*

feet and begins dodging GIFFORD'S *attempts to catch him.*)

GIFFORD   It's him.

NORA   I know it's a him. Believe you me, there's no doubt it's a him. But which him?

GIFFORD   I arrest you in the name of . . .

NORA   You've got to catch him, you fool.

(*In his excitement at the chase,* GIFFORD *temporarily loses his facility at the bugle and raises the merest squeaks in his attempts to sound the alert. The* FLASHER *dodges him and exits rapidly, right, with* GIFFORD *in pursuit still squeaking and puffing on the bugle.*)

NORA   Stop him. That beggar's been where no stranger ought to go.

(NORA *exits, right, in pursuit.* COMPO *sighs and shakes his head at the performance. He leans on a shelf, which collapses.* CLEGG *peers in and enters cautiously, left.*)

CLEGG   What's going off? What's going off?

COMPO   All in all, it's been an interesting few minutes.

(CLEGG *drags a rather bashful* FOGGY *into the room dressed in his* FLASHER *outfit.*)

CLEGG   Come in. There's nobody in here.

FOGGY   I wish there was nobody in here either.

CLEGG   It looks very lifelike. Doesn't it look very
                 lifelike.

COMPO   He's a natural. I've never seen anybody look
                 more like a flasher.

FOGGY   Shut up. You can hardly breathe in this
                 balaclava.

CLEGG   So that's why they're often breathing heavy.

                 (*They freeze in horror as* GIFFORD *rushes in,
                 right.*)

GIFFORD   I'll catch him on me Hercules bicycle.

                 (GIFFORD *too stops dead in his tracks as he
                 sees* FOGGY.)

GIFFORD   He's here.

                 (FOGGY *wails and exits rapidly, left, and
                 through the front door with* GIFFORD *in
                 pursuit.*)

GIFFORD   The bugger moves light lightning.

                 (NORA *is in the doorway, right, eyeing*
                 COMPO *and* CLEGG *suspiciously.*)

NORA   I knew it. I suspected as much. It's him,
                 isn't it. It's him that's going round exposing
                 his flashbulb. Dewhirst. Your funny friend.
                 My God! The man who's engaged to my
                 niece.

COMPO   We can explain, Nora.

NORA   Don't bother. It's all too danmed clear.
                 Me niece is engaged to some prune who's

running about wearing fresh air where his
trousers ought to be.

CLEGG   He's not, Nora. He's fully dressed
underneath.

NORA   A likely story. Don't give me that. I've been
on his knee. I know what he's wearing.
I stumbled across the truth accidentally.
Which reminds me. Where can a person
wash her hands round here?

(NORA *exits, right, with* COMPO *and* CLEGG
following.)

CLEGG   Tell her.

COMPO   Thee tell her. I think I'm facing a bit of a
credibility gap. No. I tell a lie. A hell of a
lot of credibility gap.

CLEGG   How does *she* know what the Flasher was
wearing underneath?

COMPO   I don't like to think about it.

(*They have barely exited when the front
door opens quietly and the* FLASHER *peers
in through the doorway, left. He tiptoes
into the room panting heavily. He leans
for support on the table and removes his
balaclava to wipe his brow. He puts it back
on and concentrates on trying to catch his
breath. He's too exhausted to panic much as*
NORA *re-enters, right, drying her hands. She
glares at the winded* FLASHER *and shakes her
head.*)

NORA   Look at it! Fine thing for a nephew-in-law.

(CLEGG *and* COMPO *enter behind her.*)

CLEGG   Soon as he gets his breath back he'll explain everything.

NORA   It's not me he wants to explain himself to. It's poor young woman he's promised to in marriage.

COMPO   Promised to what?

(NORA *is parading round the breathless* FLASHER, *inspecting him critically.*)

NORA   Fine thing to have in the family. We're going to look right fools when the vicar asks for his occupation.

CLEGG   Maybe you could just put self-employed.

NORA   I'll say this much for him. He's faster than Gifford Bewmont. Even on a Hercules bicycle. He was on your tail when you left here. There's more to marriage, you know, than tricky footwork.

CLEGG   Nora. If you'll just let him explain.

NORA   How can she marry an article like that? (NORA *paces agitatedly.*) I mean, do this in winter? She's going to be half her time rubbing him with Vick.

COMPO   He's fully clothed, woman. Show her, Foggy.

NORA   Don't you dare. Keep him away from me.

(COMPO *and* CLEGG *take hold of the* FLASHER *and begin unbuttoning and unbuckling his raincoat.*)

CLEGG   If you don't believe us, we'll prove it to you.

NORA	You needn't bother. I don't know what me sister's going to say.
COMPO	Listen at his breathing. He's wheezing a bit.
NORA	With his habits, I'm not surprised he's wheezing a bit.
CLEGG	For reasons which Foggy will explain as soon as he gets his breath back, he's only pretending to be the Flasher. Underneath, he's absolutely fully covered and always has been.

(*An insistent ringing on the front doorbell brings a temporary halt to the* FLASHER'S *unveiling.*)

COMPO	Now what?
CLEGG	Better go and see.

(CLEGG *pats the still-wheezing* FLASHER *on the back encouragingly, as* COMPO *goes to answer the door, left.*)

CLEGG	Hang in there, Foggy. It'll all come clear in a minute.
CONSTANCE'S VOICE	Where's me Aunty Nora? Is me Aunty Nora still here?

(CONSTANCE *enters, left, and makes straight for* NORA.)

CONSTANCE	Where've you been all this time? I've had the kettle on. I've all sorts of nearly-married sort of questions I want to ask you.

(NORA *begins to wail as she embraces her niece.*)

NORA   Oh our Connie!

CONSTANCE   There there, love. Don't cry. She always cries at weddings.

(NORA *wails even louder and hugs* CONSTANCE. COMPO *has re-entered, left. He groans quietly at* CLEGG, *who raises his own eyebrows at the noise.*)

NORA   If only you knew what you were in for?

CONSTANCE   I've got a good idea, love. Gifford wasn't that slow.

(*She sees the figure in the balaclava and gasps.*)

CONSTANCE   Who's that?

NORA   Oh you poor love. This is going to come as a shock.

(*He looks at* CLEGG. *They shrug helplessly. There's a moment's pause during which all that can be heard is the* FLASHER'S *breathing.*)

CONSTANCE   What's been happening? Who is that weird person?

(NORA *wails louder.*)

CLEGG   Tell her.

COMPO   Thee tell her.

| NORA | No. It's Aunty's painful duty to tell her. Oh our Connie. You seem fated, love, to become engaged to nothing by dozy buggers. That's your Mister Dewhirst. |

CONSTANCE   My Mister Dewhirst?

NORA   In the flesh. And when I say in the flesh I mean in the flesh.

(*Both* CONSTANCE *and* NORA *begin to wail and comfort each other.*)

CONSTANCE   My Mister Dewhirst. A flasher.

CLEGG   No he isn't.

COMPO   Honest.

CONSTANCE   Then what's he prancing around in gear like that for?

(COMPO *and* CLEGG *hurry to finish the unbuttoning of the* FLASHER'S *raincoat.*)

CLEGG   It's just a temporary disguise. Assumed for charitable purposes.

COMPO   Between thee and me, Connie, he's never had the build for anything remotely connected wi' show business.

CLEGG   There's nobody more respectable than Foggy here. See for yourself. He's fully clothed underneath.

(COMPO *and* CLEGG *open wide the* FLASHER'S *raincoat with great confidence in the direction of the two women. The women shriek.* COMPO *and* CLEGG, *startled by this*

          powerful reaction, take a peek behind the
          raincoat and hurriedly close it again.)

CLEGG   Whoops!

COMPO   Oh dear.

          (*The women begin marching for the front
          door, left.*)

NORA   Come here, Connie. We'll find you a nice
          young man with trousers on.

CONSTANCE I want Gifford Bewmont. My true love.

NORA   And you shall have him, love. Another dozy
          prong but at least he's got somewhere to put
          his bicycle clips.

          (NORA *pauses at the door, left, for a final
          glare at the three men.*)

NORA   You're weird, you lot.

          (*The women exit.* COMPO *and* CLEGG *are
          still hurriedly refastening and securing the
          raincoat.*)

CLEGG   I'll say this much for you, Foggy. When
          you're playing a part you really play the
          part.

COMPO   And it's a bigger part that I ever thought it
          would be.

          (FOGGY *enters rapidly, right, completely out
          of breath. He peels off his balaclava and
          leans against the wall unit wearily. Bits of
          it begin to collapse.* CLEGG *and* COMPO *stare
          at him with dawning comprehension. They
          begin to grin. They release the* FLASHER.)

CLEGG   Get off home and mend your ways.

FLASHER   Can I have me raincoat? He's got me
             raincoat.

             (COMPO *and* CLEGG *go to the assistance of*
             FOGGY *and begin peeling off his raincoat.*
             They are chuckling, much to the annoyance
             of the breathless FOGGY.)

FOGGY   What's so funny?

COMPO   Thee luck's in, Foggy. We've just got thee
             disengaged.

CLEGG   It's true, Foggy. You're free. She's gone
             back to Gifford Bewmont.

             (FOGGY *is overcome with gratitude. He*
             embraces them emotionally. The FLASHER
             too, until he realises his mistake as the
             FLASHER *plants a kiss on his cheek.* FOGGY
             hurriedly breaks away, tosses the raincoat
             to the FLASHER *and points to the door, left.*)

FOGGY   Get off home. The streets are clear.

CLEGG   And I don't want to worry you but I think
             your bulb's gone.

             (*They watch as the* FLASHER *exits, left. He*
             gives them a little wave. When he's gone,
             FOGGY *rubs his hands briskly.*)

FOGGY   It's times like this you find out who your
             friends are. (*He shakes them by the hand.*)
             You're sure the engagement's really off?

COMPO / CLEGG Oh we're sure. We're sure.

FOGGY   You're not just saying it. To cheer me up.

CLEGG   We're not just saying it.

COMPO   Tha's free.

FOGGY   I'm really free?

BOTH   Really free.

FOGGY   She doesn't want me any more?

COMPO   Want thee? She wouldn't touch thee wi' a
            barge pole.

FOGGY   That's marvellous. How did you do it?

            (*They look at each other.*)

CLEGG   It wasn't easy.

FOGGY   Well it wouldn't be. These things are
            damned tricky. But I want you to know
            that, whatever happens, I shall always be
            grateful. If there's anything I can ever do.
            Help yourselves to the After Dinner Mints
            you know.

            (*He shudders but hides it bravely as* COMPO
            scoops up a handful.)

COMPO   It were nothing really.

FOGGY   Don't tell me it was nothing. I'm just
            fascinated how you did it. (*He puts his arms
            round them.*) How did you manage it?

CLEGG   We'll tell you in the kitchen, Foggy.

            (*They put an arm around* FOGGY *and begin
            leading him through the door, right.*)

COMPO   Aye. I should have a cuppa tea. Tha's going
               to be ready for a cuppa tea.

CLEGG   I think we've all earned a cup of tea.
               They're funy days when you can count more
               people than trousers.

COMPO   And tha'll need thee tea strong for a while,
               Foggy, because tha'll be getting one or two
               funny looks from people.

FOGGY   Why should I get funny looks from people?

               (*They exit. A longish pause and then from
               the kitchen comes* FOGGY's *horrified shout.*)

FOGGY'S VOICE They what? They think I'm the . . . Oh my
               God!

               (COMPO's *grinning face appears at the
               serving hatch. He closes it slowly.*)

               Curtain. End.